THE BOOK O

C000258230

All proceeds from the sale of this book
go directly to *Crisis*

Charity number 1036533

THE BOOK OF STARS

Waterstone's Collection of Writing for *Crisis*

WATERSTONE'S

Published in association
with Random House

Published by Random House 1997

2 4 6 8 10 9 7 5 3 1

Selection copyright © Waterstone's Booksellers Ltd 1997
Introduction copyright © Crisis 1997

Page 88 constitutes an extension of this copyright page

First published in Great Britain by
Random House in association with Waterstone's, 1997

Random House UK Ltd
Random House, 20 Vauxhall Bridge Road, London SW1V 2SA

Random House Australia (Pty) Limited
20 Alfred Street, Milsons Point, Sydney,
New South Wales 2061, Australia

Random House New Zealand Limited
18 Poland Road, Glenfield
Auckland 10, New Zealand

Random House South Africa (Pty) Limited
Endulini, 5A Jubilee Road, Parktown 2193, South Africa

Random House UK Limited Reg. No. 954009

A CIP catalogue record for this book
is available from the British Library

ISBN 0 09 9275503

Papers used by Random House UK Ltd are natural,
recyclable products made from wood grown in
sustainable forests. The manufacturing processes
conform to the environmental regulations of the
country of origin

Typeset in 10½/12 Sabon by
MATS, Southend-on-Sea, Essex
Printed and bound in Great Britain by
Cox & Wyman Ltd, Reading, Berkshire

CRISIS

WORKING FOR HOMELESS PEOPLE

Charity number 1036533

Crisis is a national charity whose aim is to end street homelessness. It helps homeless people break out of the cycle of isolation and danger on the streets.

Crisis is best known for its work at Christmas when the charity opens thirty-five shelters for homeless people across the country. The shelters offer warmth, food, clothing, vital medical care, advice on housing and benefits as well as companionship. Christmas can be a particularly difficult and isolated time for homeless people.

Crisis continues to work throughout the year, researching the root causes of homelessness and providing emergency support on the streets as well as longer term help moving people into their own accommodation with on-going support.

Crisis relies almost entirely on donations to continue its work and the proceeds from the *Book of Stars* will contribute vital funds to ensure that the charity's work can continue this Christmas and in to the New Year.

We hope you share our concern about those who sleep rough on our streets. Such a way of life is degrading and has no place in a civilised society. We hope that in the not too distant future, Crisis will no longer be needed; but today its services are a lifeline for many. Thank you for your support.

Contents

THOUGHTS ON CHRISTMAS

Jane Asher

A sense of indefinable nostalgia for something I can never quite pin down. A mixture of joy in uncomplicated family pleasures and the selfish sadness of knowing that the thrill of feeling a heavy stocking at the bottom of my bed with outstretched toes is something I shall never know again.

Louis de Bernières

I really didn't like Christmas very much when I was young, but nowadays it strikes me as something quite precious; it is like getting a warm embrace from an old girlfriend, and feeling reassured.

John Pilger

The word 'consumer' comes from the Latin *consumere* which means 'to take up wholly, to consume, waste, squander or destroy'. This destructive force has consumed what used to be known as the Christmas spirit. It mocks the struggle of those who cannot afford to consume: like the parents of one in three children who live in poverty. We should oppose in every way Christmas's profiteers and help their victims.

Wendy Cope

Christmas wouldn't be Christmas, now, if I couldn't go and listen to Winchester Cathedral Choir singing Christmas music, especially the beautiful Hampshire carol 'Bethlehem Down'.

Meera Syal

All food is soul food so the menu would be; masala turkey, potatoes roasted in cumin seeds and garlic, puddings of every denomination, Christmas cake and almond kulfi, figgy pudding and faluda, and around the tree, diyas burning and presents bought for less than a fiver each but hand picked with care. And most importantly, family, friends, thoughts gift-wrapped for absent loved ones, stupid party games for everyone under eighty-three, soppy stuff said before the year ends so there are no regrets, ever.

Kate Atkinson

My birthday is at Christmas so I always feel that somehow Christmas has been put on specially for me. Very narcissistic!

Jonathan Coe

The ritual exchange of consumer durables, the rampant decimation of the turkey population, and falling asleep in front of films you've already seen five times before. I'm glad Christmas only comes once a year.

Arundhati Roy

Every Christmas Miss Kuriyan forced us to act in her dreadful verandah skits. My brother was always Wenceslas's slave and I a shepherd watching my flocks by night with a checked serviette on my head. Dr Pappacheu was Santa Claus. His cotton-wool beard was always sweaty and he smelled of Mylol.

John le Carré

I was fifteen, skiing in a lost valley in Switzerland. Snow had been scarce but on Christmas morning we woke to half a metre.

At the little church, the priest arrived wearing ski boots under his surplice. We would worship our Maker better on the ski slopes, he said. We agreed.

Will Self

Christmas is a hideous synergy between decadent immaterialism and material decadence . . . I avoid it and push on through to New Year.

Louis de Bernières

MRS GRIFFITHS AND THE CAROL SINGERS

MRS GRIFFITHS goes to the shop and stands next to Jack Thorn, her nose wrinkled in distaste. Jack lives with his daughter by the cricket green, in a cottage that has been handed down in his family for seven generations. Jack is the village's last peasant, and he and his house smell of 200 years of peasant life; he exudes the aromas of wet leather and horse manure, costive dogs, turnips, rainwater and cabbage water, sausages, verdigris, woollen socks, Leicester cheese, fish guts, fraying curtains, mice under the stairs, mud on the carpet, and woodlice behind the pipes, but most of all he reeks of six decades of neglected hygiene.

Jack is considered a 'character', with his teeth like tombstones, his stubble like file-card, his lips like kippers, his rolling Surrey accent, and his eyes as round as plates, but most people avoid him if they can. They moved here in search of picture-postcard England, and are uncomfortable with a real countryman who knows how to wring the neck of a chicken and has no compunction about drowning kittens in a bucket.

Jack is an anachronism, but he does not know it, and he is standing in the village shop because he has nothing to do, and not many to talk with. Every day he comes in and buys cigarette papers, so that by now he must have a roomful of them, and he engages the shop assistant in a dilatory conversation about the weather, punctuating his remarks with hawking. He used to spit it out, but nowadays he swallows it, having been roundly told off one afternoon by

Polly Wantage, the woman who wears plus-fours and shoots squirrels, and who used to play cricket for England.

'Artnoon,' he says to Mrs Griffiths 'Turned out nice again. Looks like rain though.'

'Getting chilly,' Mrs Griffiths replies.

'Time o' year,' Jack says, 'what wi' Christmas on the doorstep. Going away?'

'Staying at home. I usually do.'

'Come and eat wi' us?' Jack says, knowing that she will refuse, because everyone always does. He does not in truth want to have Mrs Griffiths for Christmas dinner, but he has always been the kind of man who tries to do his bit, the sort of fellow who will offer his sturdy back to a child who wants to climb a tree to fetch down conkers.

'Oh, I couldn't possibly,' says Mrs Griffiths shortly, without even thanking him, but Jack is not offended; he has a sense of his place in the world, and a sensible man expects snooty people to be snooty.

'Happy Christmas, then,' he says, and he touches the rim of his sagging hat. He leaves the shop and strolls home, directly across the middle of the cricket pitch. He has been asked not to, but cannot see the point of being tender in the winter about a pitch that is mangled every weekend of the summer.

Mrs Griffiths exchanges resigned glances with Mrs Davidson, whose turn it is to man the shop. It makes no profit anymore, no one would buy it from the previous owner, and now it is run on a co-operative and voluntary basis by those ladies who have time on their hands.

'I don't know why someone doesn't tell that man to wash,' Mrs Griffiths says, crossly, 'it's a disgrace.'

'Oh, I know,' Mrs Davidson says. 'Polly Wantage told him once, you know, after she stopped him from spitting, and what he said to her was unrepeatable.'

Mrs Griffiths eyes widened with a kind of horrified delight. Strong language is so far outside her world that when she overhears it, it is as exotic as Bengal tigers.

Mrs Griffiths buys a big box of Christmas cards because she wants Mrs Davidson to think that she has lots of friends and

6

relations. She will send a card to the vicar and the doctor, and she will drop one through the letter-boxes of the more respectable people in the village, so that they will send one back, and then, should anyone call round and glance at her cards, it will be clear that she is well-connected and respected.

She also buys mincemeat and ready-made frozen shortcrust pastry, because tonight she is going to make mince pies for the carol singers.

Mrs Griffiths has always hated the carol singers, even though they are the children of the better families. They arrive with their guitars and their recorders, and every year they sing the same two songs, *Silent Night* and *O Come All Ye Faithful*. They collect for the NSPCC, and Mrs Griffiths would really rather give money to the RSPCA; at least animals cannot be blamed for anything, and do not grow up to be thieves and yobs. Mrs Griffiths secretly resents the way in which the carol singers are so young and bright-eyed, so full of high laughter, so full of the future, and in the past she has always turned out the lights when she heard them coming, so that she does not have to go out and listen to them, or give them money, or make mince pies and hot punch as everyone else does. The carol singers have always sung to her closed door and dowsed lights, and have then departed.

But things have changed. Mrs Griffiths lost her husband in the spring, and is slowly realising that at last the time has come when she has to make an effort to get on with people. She did not love her husband, he was boring and inconsequential, and she had not even loved him when they married. After he died, she felt merely a sense of relief, conjoined with the bitterness of a freedom that has come too late. Sometimes she wonders whether she has ever loved anyone at all, and certainly she has never loved anyone as they do on the television late at night, with all those heaving backsides and that groaning. But, even though her husband was a cipher, nowadays Mrs Griffiths feels a certain emptiness, a certain need to reach out, a certain need to be reborn.

Tonight she will make mince pies and punch, she will leave

the lights on, she will come out and listen, and she will tell the children that their music is wonderful. She will ignore the fact that they know only one verse of *Silent Night*, their guitars are out of tune and their recorders too shrill, and she will wish them a happy Christmas even though they are beautiful and still have a chance in life.

Mrs Griffiths covers herself and her kitchen in dusting sugar, she deals with the frustration of pastry that sticks to the table and the rolling pin, she conquers the meanness that nearly prevents her from pouring a whole bottle of red wine into the punch, and then she waits, sitting on the wooden chair in the kitchen, warmed by the rich smells of baking pastry and hot wine, and lemon, and rum. 'After they've been,' she thinks, 'I will write all my cards, and then I'll draw a hot bath and read.' Since her husband died, Mrs Griffiths has taken to reading true-life romances that one can order six at a time from a special club. She has read so many that she thinks she could probably write one herself.

It grows very dark, and three hours pass by. Mrs Griffiths goes often to her door, and opens it, to see if she can hear the carol singers coming. The night is very cold, there is a frosty wind, but she does not think that it is going to rain. They will be here before long.

Mrs Griffiths sits in her wooden chair and thinks about what she should say to the children; does Merry Christmas sound better than Happy Christmas, or vice-versa? Does 'Thank you so much for coming' sound too formal? The young are not very formal these days. During the time when everyone was going on about the Beatles, the youngsters kept saying 'groovy', but that was probably not very with it anymore. She experiments with 'Groovy Christmas', but decides against it. There is no point in pretending.

Mrs Griffiths hears *Silent Night* in the distance. The children are singing to the gypsies in their scrapyard that is full of oil and mud and raffish alsatian dogs. Now they are singing to the Davidsons, and now they are singing to the mad musicologist, and now they are singing to smelly Jack Thorn. Mrs Griffiths listens hard for the squeak of her garden gate and the experimental chords of the guitarists. She knows that, in between the houses, the children bray out songs from pop groups with silly names and working-class accents. The children arrive at the garden gate, and the tall lanky one says 'What about this one?'

'Not worth it,' says the other guitarist, who is proud of the fact that he is going to get a shaving kit for Christmas. He strokes his invisible moustache with a nail-bitten forefinger.

'She's an old skinflint,' says the blonde girl who will be beautiful when she loses her puppy fat. 'Her husband died,' says the dark, sensitive girl with the brown eyes.

'It won't do any harm, will it?' asks the blonde girl.

'There's no point,' says the lanky boy, 'she just turns off the lights as soon as she hears us coming. Every year it's the same, don't you remember? She's an old ratbag.'

'Mum told us not to leave her out,' says the blonde.

'Who's going to tell Mum?' demands her brother, 'Let's go and do the Armstrongs.'

Mrs Griffiths sits on her wooden chair and hears *Silent Night* coming from next door. At first she feels a livid pang of anger, and one or two of those vehement forbidden words spring to her mind, but not to her lips. She is indignant, and thinks: 'How dare they miss me out? They always come here. Why have they chosen me to be the one to miss out?' She looks at her inviting heap of mince pies and her steaming bowl of punch, and thinks 'And I did all this for them.' She wants to go outside and shout insults at them, but she cannot think of anything that would not sound ridiculous and undignified.

Alongside her anger and frustration, Mrs Griffiths abruptly feels more tired and forlorn than she has ever felt in her life, and she begins to cry for the first time that she can remember since she was a child. She is surprised by large tears that well up in her eyes and slide down he sides of her nose, rolling down her hands and wrists, and down into her sleeves. She had not remembered that tears could be so hot. She tastes one, in order to be reminded of their saltiness, and finds it comforting. She thinks, 'Perhaps I should get a cat,' and fetches some kitchen roll so that she can blow her nose.

Mrs Griffiths begins to write her cards. One for the vicar, one for the doctor, one for the people in the mansion, one for the conservative councillor. She gets up from her chair, and, without really thinking about it, eats a mince pie and takes a glass of punch. She had forgotten how good they can be, and she feels the punch igniting her insides. The sensuality of it shocks and seduces her, and she takes another glass.

Mrs Griffiths cries some more, but this time it is partly for pleasure, for the pleasure of the hot, briny water, and the sheer self-indulgence. A rebellious whim creeps up on her. She glances around as if to check that she is truly alone in the house, and then she stands up and shouts:

'Bloody bloody bloody bloody bloody.' She adds: 'Bloody children, bloody bloody.' She attempts 'bollocks' but merely embarrasses herself, and tries 'bugger' instead. She drinks more punch and says 'bloody bugger'. She writes a card to the gypsies who own the scrapyard, and to the water board man who had an illegitimate child by a Swedish barmaid. She eats two mince pies at once, cramming them into her mouth, one on top of the other, and the crumbs and the sugar settle on to the front of her cardigan. She fetches a biscuit tin, and puts into it six of the remaining pies. She presses down the lid and ventures out into the night.

When she returns she finishes off the punch, and then heaves herself upstairs with the aid of the banisters. She is beginning to feel distinctly ill, and heads for her bed with the unconscious but unswerving instinct of a homing pigeon. She reminds herself to draw the curtains so that no one will be able to pry and spy, and then she undresses with difficulty, and throws her clothes on to the floor with all the perverse but justified devilment of one who has been brought up not to, and has never tried it before. She extinguishes the light and crawls into bed, but every time that she closes her eyes she begins to feel seasick. Her eyes glitter in the dark like those of a small girl, the years are briefly annulled, and she remembers how to feel frightened when an owl hoots outside.

At eleven-thirty, fetid Jack Thorn comes out of his front door to put the cat out, and spots a biscuit tin by the doorscraper. He picks it up, curious, and takes it back inside. 'Look what some'un left,' he says to his daughter, who is just as unkempt as he is, but smells more sweetly.

'Well, open it,' she says.

Jack prises off the lid with his thick yellow nails, and inside he finds six mince pies, and an envelope. Jack feels a leap of excitement and pleasure in his belly, and hands the card to his daughter to read. It says, 'To dear Mr Jack Thorn and daughter, a very Happy Christmas and New Year, from Marjorie Griffiths.'

'Well, bugger me,' say's Jack Thorn, and his daughter says 'Now there's a turn-up for the books.' Jack puts the card on the mantelpiece, crams a whole mince pie into his mouth, and delves among the clutter for a pencil, and the box of cards that he bought from the village shop three years ago.

Louis de Bernières is the author of several novels, including *Captain Corelli's Mandolin*, published by Minerva.

Victoria Mather
and Sue Macartney-Snape

SOCIAL STEREOTYPE 164:
THE LAST MINUTE
CHRISTMAS SHOPPER

Timothy wasn't going to buy any Christmas presents at all, throughout December he has nurtured – and expounded – the cogent views on materialism and commercialism consistent with spending the holiday in Thailand with his girlfriend. Unfortunately, she then dumped him. So he's going to his sister's and it is now, on Christmas Eve, in the last petrol station before her chill house in Northamptonshire, that Tim hovers desperately between dog food and jump leads. Seriously at the wrong end of his fashionably cool cynicism about the Christmas spirit, he is wondering how to counteract Granny's handkerchief offensive. And can he fob his mother off with a three-pack of 20 denier tights in an alarming shade of Brazil nut? His sister has very strong views about children and sweets, so the Cadbury's Christmas stocking adorned with cellophane robins will not impress and probably be stolen by the labrador. It is with relief unequalled since Mafeking that he finds a multi-beamed torch which seemingly doubles as an arc light – perfect for his brother-in-law's obsession with the innards of his tractor. Blessedly, the off-licence in the village is still open – Timothy clears the shelves of champagne and Old Sporran malt whisky and hands over his credit card. On Christmas morning, when his sister says briskly. 'We weren't really expecting you, Tim, so we haven't got you anything special', he feels unaccountably disappointed.

Victoria Mather and Sue Macartney-Snape's
Absolutely Typical and *Absolutely Typical Too*
are published by Methuen.

Sue Townsend

ADRIAN MOLE'S CHRISTMAS

Tuesday   December 22nd   1981

School was closed this morning because the teachers couldn't
manage to get in on time because of the snow. That will teach
them to live in old mill houses and windmills out in the
country! Miss Elf lives with a West Indian in a terraced house
in the town, so she bravely turned out to prepare for the
school concert in the afternoon. I decided to forgive Pandora
for the fox fur in the cat's basket incident after she had
pointed out that the cat was an expectant mother.

The school concert was not a success. The bell-ringing from
class One-G went on too long, my father said 'The Bells! The
Bells!', and my mother laughed too loudly and made Mr
Scruton look at her.

The school orchestra was a disaster! My mother said,
'When are they going to stop tuning-up and start playing?' I
told her that they had just played a Mozart horn concerto.
That made my mother and father and Pandora's mother and
father start laughing in a very unmannerly fashion. When ten-
stone Alice Bernard from Three-C came on stage in a tutu and
did the dying swan I thought my mother would explode. Alice
Bernard's mother led the applause, but not many people
followed.

The Dumbo class got up and sang a few boring old carols.
Barry Kent sang all the vulgar versions (I know because I was
watching his lips) then they sat down cross-legged, and brain-
box Henderson from Five-K played a trumpet, Jew's harp,
piano and guitar. The smarmy git looked dead superior when
he was bowing during his applause. Then it was the interval

14

and time for me to change into my white T-shirt-and-Wranglers Joseph costume. The tension backstage was electric. I stood in the wings (a theatrical term – it means the side of the stage) and watched the audience filing back into their places. Then the music from *Close Encounters* boomed out over the stereo speakers, and the curtains opened on an abstract manger and I just had time to whisper to Pandora 'Break a leg, darling', before Miss Elf pushed us out into the lights. My performance was brilliant! I really got under the skin of Joseph but Pandora was less good, she forgot to look tenderly at Jesus/Peter Brown.

The three punks/wise men made too much noise with their chains and spoiled my speech about the Middle East situation, and the angels representing Mrs Thatcher got hissed by the audience so loudly that their spoken chorus about unemployment was wasted.

Still, all in all, it was well received by the audience. Mr Scruton got up and made a hypocritical speech about 'a brave experiment' and 'Miss Elf's tireless work behind the scenes', and then we all sang 'We wish you a Merry Christmas'!

Driving home in the car my father said, 'That was the funniest Nativity play I have ever seen. Whose idea was it to turn it into a comedy?' I didn't reply. It wasn't a comedy.

Wednesday   December 23rd

9 a.m. Only two shopping days left for Christmas and I am still penniless. I have made a Blue Peter oven-glove for Miss Elf but in order to give it to her in time for Christmas I will have to go into the ghetto and risk getting mugged.

I will have to go out carol singing, there is nothing else I can do to raise finance.

10 p.m. Just got back from carol singing. The suburban houses were a dead loss. People shouted, 'Come back at Christmas', without even opening the door. My most appreciative audience were the drunks staggering in and out of the Black Bull. Some of them wept openly at the beauty of my solo rendition of 'Silent Night'. I must say that I presented a touching picture as I stood in the snow with my young face lifted to the heavens ignoring the scenes of drunken revelry around me.

I made £3.13½ plus an Irish tenpence and a Guinness bottle-top. I'm going out again tomorrow. I will wear my school uniform, it should be worth a few extra quid.

Thursday   December 24th

Took Bert's Woodbines round to the home. Bert is hurt because I haven't been to see him. He said he didn't want to spend Christmas with a lot of malicious old women. Him and Queenie are causing a scandal. They are unofficially engaged. They have got their names on the same ashtray. I have invited Bert and Queenie for Christmas Day. My mother doesn't know yet but I'm sure she won't mind, we have got a big turkey. I sang a few carols for the old ladies. I made two pounds eleven pence out of them so I went to Woolworth's to buy Pandora's Chanel No. 5. They hadn't got any so I bought her an underarm deodorant instead.

The house looks dead clean and sparkling, there is a magic smell of cooking and satsumas in the air. I have searched around for my presents but they are not in the usual places. I want a racing bike, nothing else will please me. It's time I was independently mobile.

11 p.m. Just got back from the Black Bull. Pandora came with me, we wore our school uniforms and reminded all the drunks of their own children. They coughed up conscience money to the tune of twelve pounds fifty-seven! So we are going to see a pantomime on Boxing Day and we will have a family bar of Cadbury's Dairy Milk each!

Friday   December 25th
CHRISTMAS DAY

Got up at 5 a.m. to have a ride on my racing bike. My father paid for it with American Express. I couldn't ride it far because of the snow, but it didn't matter. I just like looking at it. My father had written on the gift tag attached to the handlebars, 'Don't leave it out in the rain this time' – as if I would!

My parents had severe hangovers, so I took them breakfast in bed and gave them my presents at the same time. My mother was overjoyed with her egg timer and my father was equally delighted with his bookmark, in fact everything was going OK until I casually mentioned that Bert and Queenie were my guests for the day, and would my father mind getting out of bed and picking them up in his car.

The row went on until the lousy Sugdens arrived. My grandma and grandad Sugden and Uncle Dennis and his wife Marcia and their son Maurice all look the same, as if they went to funerals every day of their lives. I can hardly believe that my mother is related to them. The Sugdens refused a drink and had a cup of tea whilst my mother defrosted the turkey in the bath. I helped my father carry Queenie (fifteen stone) and Bert (fourteen stone) out of our car. Queenie is one of those loud types of old ladies who dye their hair and try to look young. Bert is in love with her. He told me when I was helping him into the toilet.

Grandma Mole and Auntie Susan came at twelve-thirty and pretended to like the Sugdens. Auntie Susan told some amusing stories about life in prison but nobody but me and my father and Bert and Queenie laughed.

I went up to the bathroom and found my mother crying and running the turkey under the hot tap. She said, 'The bloody thing won't thaw out, Adrian. What am I going to do?' I said, 'Just bung it in the oven'. So she did.

We sat down to eat Christmas dinner four hours late. By then my father was too drunk to eat anything. The Sugdens enjoyed the Queen's Speech but nothing else seemed to please them. Grandma Sugden gave me a book called *Bible Stories for Boys*. I could hardly tell her that I had lost my faith, so I said thank-you and wore a false smile for so long that it hurt.

The Sugdens went to their camp beds at ten o'clock. Bert, Queenie and my mother and father played cards while I polished my bike. We all had a good time making jokes about the Sugdens. Then my father drove Bert and Queenie back to the home and I phoned Pandora up and told her that I loved her more than life itself.

I am going round to her house tomorrow to give her the deodorant and escort her to the pantomime.

Saturday December 26th
BANK HOLIDAY IN UK AND REP. OF IRELAND
(a day may be given in lieu). NEW MOON

Sugdens got up at 7 a.m. and sat around in their best clothes looking respectable. I went out on my bike. When I got back my mother was still in bed, and my father was arguing with Grandad Sugden about our dog's behaviour, so I went for another ride.

I called in on Grandma Mole, ate four mince pies, then rode back home. I got up to 30 mph on the dual carriageway, it was dead good. I put my new suede jacket and corduroy trousers on (courtesy of my father's Barclaycard) and called for Pandora; she gave me a bottle of after-shave for my Christmas present. It was a proud moment, it signified the *End of Childhood*.

We quite enjoyed the pantomime but it was rather childish for our taste. Bill Ash and Carole Hayman were good as Aladdin and the Princess, but the robbers played by Jeff Teare and Ian Giles were best. Sue Pomeroy gave a hilarious performance as Widow Twankey. In this she was greatly helped by her cow, played by Chris Martin and Lou Wakefield.

Sunday   December 27th
1ST AFTER CHRISTMAS

The Sugdens have gone back to Norfolk, thank God!

The house is back to its usual mess. My parents took a bottle of vodka and two glasses to bed with them last night. I haven't seen them since.

Went to Melton Mowbray on my bike, did it in five hours.

18

Tuesday   December 21st   1983

Last day of school

Thank God! I got seven Christmas cards. Three tasteful. Four in putrid taste and printed on flimsy rubbish paper that won't stand up. On receipt I quickly wrote out seven cards and gave them to a passing elf. Mr Golightly, director of the Christmas play, *The Importance Of Being Ernest Christmas Show*, was very irritable today when I wished him good luck for tonight. He said, 'Thanks to your abdication, Adrian, I have got a midget playing Ernest.' (Peter Brown, whose mother smoked throughout her pregnancy!)

I'm glad I did abdicate from my role, because the play was a complete fiasco. Lady Bracknell forgot to say, 'A handbag?' And Peter Brown stood behind a chair so that the audience only saw the top of his head. Simone Bates, as Gwendoline, was quite good but what a shame her costume didn't hide her tattoos! The other parts are just not worth writing about.

The best thing in the show was the scenery. I congratulated Mr Animba, the woodwork teacher, on his dedication. He said, 'Do you think anybody noticed that it was adapted from the *Peter Pan* scenery of three years ago?' I assured him that nobody had complained that the view from the French windows was of a palm-fringed island.

Mr Golightly was nowhere to be seen at the end of the play. Somebody told me that he had run from the wings shortly before the end, saying he had to visit his mother in hospital.

The best thing about the evening was the interval when Pandora played her viola in the refreshment room.

Wednesday   December 22nd

Drew £15 out of my Building Society today.

I know it's a lot but I've got an extra person to buy for: Rosie.

9.30 p.m. Forgot that Queenie isn't here any more. I needn't have been so extravagant. My memory!

Thursday   December 23rd

Made a list and went to Woolworth's, as they have got a good selection of festive gifts.

Dog	False bone	(£1.25)
Pandora	Solid gold chain	(£2.00)
Mother	Egg Timer	(About £1.59)
Rosie	Chocolate Santa	(79p)
Bert	20 Woodbines	(£1.09)
Nigel	He gets nothing this year	His best friend is now Clive Barnes
Father	Festive tin of anti-freeze	(£1.39)
Grandma	Gift pack of dusters	(£1.29)
Auntie Susan	Hankie Set	(99p)
Sabre	Dog Comb	(£1.29)

Woolworth's was swarming with last-minute shoppers, so I had to queue for half an hour at the checkout till. Why do people wait to do their shopping until there are only two days left before Christmas?

I couldn't get on a bus home because of the stupid lemmings. Went to the 'Off the Streets' Youth Club party with Pandora. Nigel caused a scandal by dancing with Clive Barnes who was wearing lipstick and mascara!

Everyone was saying that Nigel is gay, so I made sure that everyone knew that he is no longer my best friend. Barry Kent smuggled two cans of 'Tartan' bitter through the fire doors. His gang of six shared them, and got leglessly drunk. At the end of the party Rick Lemon put 'White Christmas' by some old crumblie on the record deck and all the couples danced romantically together. I told Pandora how much I adored her and she said, 'Aidy, my pet, how long will our happiness last?'

Trust Pandora to put a damp cloth on everything. Saw her home. Kissed her twice. Went home. Fed dog. Checked Rosie's pulse. Went to bed.

Friday   December 24th
CHRISTMAS EVE

My mother is being kept a prisoner by Rosie; so I have had to do all the Christmas preparations. I was up at 7.30 queuing in the butcher's for a fresh turkey, pork joint, and sausage meat.

By 9 a.m. I was in the queue at the greengrocer's: 3lbs sprouts, 24 tangerines, 2lbs mixed nuts, 2 bunches of holly (make sure they have berries), salad (don't forget green pepper), 2 boxes of dates (get those with camel on lid), 3lbs of apples (if no Cox's get G. Smith), 6lbs potatoes (check each one for signs of sprouting).

By 11.15 I was in the launderette washing and drying the loose covers off the three-piece suite.

2 p.m. saw me at the grocer's with a long list, and Rosie's pram outside to cart everything home. £2.50's worth of Stilton (make sure good blue colour, firm texture), 2 boxes sponge fingers, red and yellow jelly . . . tin of fruit salad. . . . It went on for ever.

At 4.10 p.m. I was struggling into Woolworth's front doors, and trying to fight my way to the fairy-light counter. At 4.20 I got to the counter only to find empty shelves and other desperate people swapping rumours: 'Curry's have got some lantern style', 'Rumbelow's have got two packets of the "star type"', 'Habitat have got the High Tech styles but they're pricey!'

I went to all the above shops and more, but at 5 p.m. I admitted defeat and joined the long queue at the bus stop.

Drunken youths covered in 'crazy foam' and factory girls wearing tinsel garlands paraded around the town singing carols. Jesus would have turned in his tomb.

At 5.25 I had a panic attack and left the queue and rushed into Marks and Spencer's to buy something.

I was temporarily deranged. A voice inside my head kept saying: 'Only five minutes before the shops shut. Buy! Buy! Buy!'

The shop was full of sweating men buying women's underwear. At 5.29 I came to my senses, and went back to bus stop. Just in time to see the bus leaving. I got home at 6.15 after buying a packet of fairy lights from Cherry's shop which is just around the corner from our house.

My mother has made the lounge look especially nice (she'd even dusted the skirting board) and when the new fairy lights were switched on, and the fruit arranged, and the holly stuck up etc, it looked like a room on a Christmas card. Me and my mother had a quick drink before Bert arrived in an Age Concern car, driven by a kind volunteer.

We settled him in front of the telly with a beetroot sandwich and a bottle of brown ale, and we went into the kitchen to start the mincepies and trifles.

1 a.m. Just got back from the Midnight Service. It was very moving (even for an atheist), though I think it was a mistake to have a live donkey in the church.

2 a.m. Just remembered, forgot to buy nutcrackers.

Saturday   December 25th
CHRISTMAS DAY

Got up at 7.30.

Had a wash and a shave, cleaned teeth, squeezed spots then went downstairs and put kettle on. I don't know what's happened to Christmas Day lately, but something has. It's just not the same as it used to be when I was a kid. My mother fed and cleaned Rosie, and I did the same to Bert. Then we went into the lounge and opened our presents. I was dead disappointed when I saw the shape of my present. I could tell at a glance that it didn't contain a single microchip. OK a sheepskin coat is warm but there's nothing you can *do* with it except wear it.

In fact after only two hours of wearing it, I got bored and took it off. However, my mother was ecstatic about her egg timer; she said, 'Wow, another one for my collection.' Rosie ignored the chocolate Santa I bought her. That's 79 pence wasted! *This is what I got:*

¾ length sheepskin coat (out of Littlewoods catalogue)

Beano Annual (a sad disappointment, this year's is very childish)

Slippers (like Michael Caine wears, although not many people know that)

Swiss army knife (my father is hoping I'll go out into the fresh air and use it)

Tin of humbugs (supposedly from the dog)

Knitted Balaclava helmet (from Grandma Mole. Yuk! Yuk!)

Boys' Book of Sport (from Grandma Sugden: Stanley Matthews on cover)

I was glad when Auntie Susan and her friend Gloria turned up; at 11 o'clock. Their talk is very metropolitan and daring; and Gloria is dead glamorous and sexy. She wears frilly dresses, and lacy tights, and high heels. And she's got an itsy-bitsy voice that makes my stomach go soft. Why she's friends with Auntie Susan, who is a prison warder, smokes Panama cigars and has got hairy fingers, I'll never know.

The turkey was OK. But would have been better if the giblets and the plastic bag had been removed before cooking. Bert made chauvinist remarks during the carving. He leered at Gloria's cleavage and said, 'Give me a nice piece of breast.' Gloria wasn't a bit shocked, but I went dead red, and pretended that I'd dropped my cracker under the table.

When my mother asked me which part of the turkey I wanted, I said, 'A wing please!' I really wanted breast, leg, or thigh. But wing was the only part of the bird without sexual connotations. Rosie had a few spoons of mashed potato and gravy. Her table manners are disgusting, even worse than Bert's.

I was given a glass of Bull's Blood wine and felt dead sensual. I talked brilliantly and with consummate wit for an hour, but then my mother told me to leave the table, saying, 'One sniff of the barmaid's apron and his mouth runs away with him.'

The Queen didn't look very happy when she was giving her speech. Perhaps she got lousy Christmas presents this year, like me. Bert and Auntie Susan had a disagreement about the Royal Family. Bert said he would 'move the whole lot of 'em into council houses in Liverpool.'

Gloria said, 'Oh Bert that's a bit drastic. Milton Keynes would be more suitable. They're not used to roughing it you know.'

In the evening I went round to see Grandma and my father. Grandma forced me to eat four mincepies, and asked me why I wasn't wearing my new Balaclava helmet. My father didn't say anything; he was dead drunk in an armchair.

Sunday   December 26th
FIRST AFTER CHRISTMAS

Pandora and I exchanged presents in a candlelit ceremony in my bedroom. I put the solid gold chain round her neck, and she put a 70% wool, 10% cashmere, 20% acrylic scarf round my neck.

A cashmere scarf at fifteen!

I'll make sure the label can be seen by the public at all times.

Pandora went barmy about the solid gold chain. She kept looking at herself in the mirror, she said, 'Thank you, darling, but how on earth can you afford solid gold? It must have cost you at least a hundred pounds!'

I didn't tell her that Woolworth's were selling them cheap at two pounds a go.

Monday   December 27th
BOXING DAY, HOLIDAY (UK EXCEPT SCOTLAND).
HOLIDAY (CANADA). BANK HOLIDAY (SCOTLAND).
HOLIDAY (REP OF IRELAND)

Just had a note handed to me from a kid riding a new BMX.

> Dear heart,
> I'm awfully sorry but I will have to cancel our trip to the cinema to see *ET*.

24

I woke up this morning with an ugly disfiguring rash around my neck.

Yours sincerely,

Pandora

P.S. I am allergic to non-precious metal.

Sue Townsend's Adrian Mole books and her new novel, *Ghost Children*, are published by Methuen.

John Farman

BAH – HUMBUG! – OR THE STORY OF CHRISTMAS PAST

To perceive Christmas through its wrapping becomes more difficult every year Elwyn Brooks White (1803)

I, for one, am getting just a little fed up with that sort of talk. There are too many cynics out there trying to cast dark shadows over all that is most ancient and meaningful in our lives. Don't you, like me, feel an uncanny tingle as Christmas approaches? All those nostalgic tinkly tunes in our shops and public places; kindly toymakers presenting their wondrous polypropylene wares to our telly-glued little folk; the anticipation that builds as we fill our fridges, freezers and larders to bursting for the two days of fabulous feasting ahead.

But, most of all, isn't Christmas a time to look back – to remember the birth of baby Jesus in a humble stable and all that went with it? Next they'll be questioning the validity of dear old Father Christmas, his faithful reindeers and rooftop aerobics, the stocking and the rest of the accompanying festive fun, purely because it appears he was only thought up in eighteen hundred and something and imported from the USA (as if we'd ever copy anything from them).

Cynical historians would even have us question the Christian origins of our celebrations, delighting in informing us that the great occasion itself was invented by those wicked Roman Emperors. Clever bods claim, that while Christians were just a twinkle in the wild Roman beasts' eyes, they chose December 25 as the birthday of Sol Invictus (unconquered sun). Also, they'd like us to believe that it was the season of Saturnalia, when anyone who was anyone in Rome went on

an endless drunken binge, playing the forerunners of our exciting Christmas games (albeit ruder versions) and exchanging little gifts like sweetmeats and slaves. As for the crib and all its ancillary accessories; they reckon the Christians got the idea from the long lost cult of Adonis. What heresy! Everyone knows the drinking and fun was invented by twentieth-century *homo sapiens*!

And would you credit this. Other, even more boring people tell us that in Northern Europe, way back in the Middle Ages, Christmas was known as the Yule Festival and that that's where all the trees, holly and mistletoe come from. Twelfth Night, apparently, was the frenzied climax to a twelve day pagan rave-up which, much later, those guardians of our morality, the Puritans, tried their level best to put a stop to. Actually, they succeeded in Scotland, which is why they now only celebrate the New Year.

The whole greenery thing, came back into common use in 1840, followed twenty years later by Christmas cards, paper decorations, crackers and all the tinselly stuff. Honestly, they make it sound as the whole package is just a commercially hyped-up Victorian extravaganza. And they won't even let us have our Christmas dinner in peace. Turkeys, they claim, once slept tranquilly as December approached, because the traditional meal had always been roast beef or goose – the huge birds only flapped over from Mexico in Henry VIII's day. These historical saddos now have the cheek to suggest that we probably borrowed our traditional dinner from the American's Thanksgiving shin dig (yet another import).

Just because Christmas has had so much superfluous junk bolted on to it over the years, some people think they have the right to claim that it has become simply a shallow media exercise – a convenient way of shifting a load of unwanted gear (and gut-wrenching sentiment). For them the whole Christmas experience had become, as Elwyn White suggested at the beginning – all top hat and no rabbit. What Rubbish! Let's put on 'Santa Meets the Spice Girls' now – we'll show 'em!

John Farmen's *The Very Bloody History of Britain*
is published by Red Fox.

Jane Green

A CHRISTMAS STORY

RIDICULOUS ISN'T IT? I stopped believing in Father
Christmas when I was about six years old, yet I still believe in
knights in shining armour.

Well, not as a rule, perhaps, but somewhere out there I'm
still convinced there is a tall, dark handsome stranger who is
waiting to whisk me off my feet, and if his armour's slightly
tarnished, so what? I'm thirty years old for God's sake. I'm
expected to compromise slightly.

And yes, I only mention Christmas because it's that bloody
time of year again. Christmas. Magical for kids, romantic for
couples, and miserable as hell if, like me, once again you're on
your own.

Every year I tell myself the same thing. That if by 1
December next year I'm still single, I'm going to go out with
anyone, absolutely anyone, just so I don't have to spend the
damn thing on my own again.

And every year, right around 2 December, I realise that
there simply aren't any men around, decent or otherwise, so
now I've just resigned myself.

Actually, there is something I've done slightly different this
year, but it's not something I'm revealing to all and sundry
because I'm not particularly proud of it, but nor am I
particularly proud of being single, and I remember someone
once saying that it's all a numbers game – the more men you
meet, the more chance you have – so I joined a dating agency.

I know, I know. I thought they were for sad, desperate
losers too, but the woman in the office was really nice, really
normal, and although I haven't met anyone yet, she's

convinced there are some lovely men, and perhaps in the new year, she says, someone perfect will come along.

Oh, I'm sorry,. I haven't introduced myself yet, have I? As you know, I'm thirty. As you also know, I'm single and sick to bloody death of it. You may or may not care to know that my name is Nina, that I work in advertising, and that I have no cats, but only because I figure that if you're in my position and you have cats, you're only a small step away from pushing all your belongings around in plastic bags in a Waitrose trolley.

I live with Suzy in a smallish flat in Belsize Park, and although parking's a complete nightmare if you're stupid enough to arrive home after six p.m., we like it. It works for us.

Suzy was my partner in crime, but needless to say Suzy's now in love, and the rare occasions she's home she just moons about from room to room with a sickly smile on her face, and although I'm pleased for her, of *course* I'm pleased for her, I don't personally think that James is anywhere near good enough for her. She might think his childish jokes and high-pitched giggle are endearing, but I find them a pain in the arse.

Luckily he's not around that much. Unluckily neither is she, and if I wasn't so determined to live up to my spinster label, I'd be out choosing kittens right this moment. Anything to have some bloody company.

'Laura?' She sounds as if I should know her, but I swear I don't know anyone called Laura.

'From the dating agency.'

'Oh Laura! Hi!' My heart skips a beat. Could she possibly have found me a man for Christmas on the eve of Christmas itself. Well, morning of the eve of Christmas itself, if I'm more accurate. Could this be the present I've been waiting for all my life?

'Look I know this is short notice,' she says, sounding half nervous and half excited, 'but someone's just signed up who I think might be perfect for you, and I've shown him your details and he's desperate to meet you.'

'Oh my God! This is so exciting! What's he like?'

'Well before I tell you, the catch is that he wants to meet you tonight for an early dinner, because Christmas, apparently, is enormously busy for him workwise, and he doesn't think he'll be able to see you for a while if it's not tonight.'

'Tonight's fine,' I say, forgetting that you are definitely not supposed to admit to staying in on Christmas Eve. Not even if you're staying in with a tub of Ben & Jerry's, two bottles of claret, and the entire contents of the partyfoods section from your local M&S in the fridge.

'Oh that's wonderful!' she says. 'He'll be so pleased. He thought that perhaps you might like to meet him for a drink at Saint at seven o'clock.'

'Yeah, I can do that. But what's he like? Tell me about him.'

'He's self-employed, apparently with an extremely successful business, and he's slightly older than I would normally put you with, but you did say you liked older men . . .'

'How much older exactly?'

'Not sure offhand. Hang on, let me find my notes.'

'Don't worry,' I say. 'I'll find out for myself soon enough. What's his name?'

'Nick.'

Nick. A good name. A strong, sexy, masculine name. Yes, I think. I could definitely see myself with someone called Nick. Nick and Nina. Nina and Nick. I like it very much indeed.

'And how will I know him?' I say, trying to push away visions of white carnations and the *Evening Standard* tucked furtively under one arm.

'He says not to worry, he'll find you. Oh, my line's bleeping, can you hang on?'

'Don't worry,' I say, because there are preparations to be made for my Christmas Eve date, 'you go. I'll ring you tomorrow and let you know how it went.'

'Not tomorrow!' she laughs. 'It's Christmas!'

'Oh God,' I groan. 'I was trying to forget. Listen, have a great Christmas and I'll speak to you in the new year.'

'And you,' she says warmly, and quickly, because she's obviously desperate to get her call waiting before they ring off. 'And fingers crossed he's Mr Right.'

Yup, I think as I put down the phone. Fingers crossed.

So here I am now, hair freshly washed and swinging in the soft glow of the spotlight above my head, make-up perfectly applied, new designer red trouser suit (it is Christmas, for God's sake), and I'm nervous as hell.

Just for a change I'm surrounded by couples, and groups of beautiful, trendy people evidently on their last get-together before travelling home later tonight for Christmas, and nowhere is there a single man, by himself, looking as if he's looking for me.

So I sigh, look at my watch for the eighth time in the last two minutes – because, God, I don't want anyone to think I'm here on my own – and take another sip of my mulled wine.

'Nina?'

Oh shit. Oh no. Oh Christ. Someone made a terrible mistake. This is not funny, this is bloody terrible, and as disappointment flicks over my eyes, I make a mental note that on 1 January am going to kill Laura. *Kill*. Plus, I'm going to get a full refund. What the hell was she thinking of? And more to the point, what the hell was I thinking of, seriously hoping that a dating agency would be the answer.

For standing in front of me is my grandfather. Well, OK, not exactly my grandfather, but he's so old he might as well be. A short, rotund – OK then, fat, white-haired OLD MAN. He's so old his hair's completely white, and not only that, he's got a bloody beard as well.

I mean Jesus, what is going on here?

I'm so shocked I can't say anything, and he just smiles at me, eyes twinkling away, and I look at him and think if I were forty years older I'd probably find him incredibly attractive, but oh my God, this man is so *old*.

'May I?' he says, pulling the chair next to me out, while I just nod, gulp, and then try and compose my features because I'm a well-brought up girl, and whilst I wouldn't let this man touch me if my life depended on it, nor am I going to be rude enough to get up and walk out. Even if that's exactly what I'd like to do.

'Can I get you a drink?' he says, looking at my wine.

'No thank you,' I say stiffly. 'I'm fine.'

'Ah. Well. I'm Nick,' he says, extending his hand, and I reluctantly shake hands and wonder how soon I could politely get away.

'I can't stay that long I'm afraid,' I say, 'I suddenly realised that I have a Christmas drinks thing tonight . . . I'm so sorry.'

'Not to worry,' he says cheerfully, 'I'm working later tonight anyway, so it can't be a late night for me either.'

Now what on earth was this man thinking of, wanting to meet someone who's thirty? Under any other circumstances I'd be thinking he was just a dirty old man, but sitting here he looks rather sweet. Well, put it like this, he looks like he'd be a perfect grandfather.

'So what do you do?' I say, desperately trying to think of something to say.

'Ah.' He smiles, leaning back and resting his hands on his paunch, and let me tell you, his paunch is huge. HUGE. Yeuch. 'I'm self-employed. I suppose you would say I'm in the import/export business, although at the moment I'm concentrating more on the export side.'

Great. This goes from bad to worse. At the very least he would have to be a multi-millionaire to engage my interest, but no. He's in import bloody export. Fascinating. Not.

'And you're working tonight? Christmas Eve?' I continue politely. God, wouldn't my parents be proud of me.

'Christmas Eve is the busiest night of the year,' he nods, before swiftly changing the subject. Obviously not a man who likes talking about his work. 'Nina dear, seeing as we can't stay that long,' he says, 'how about we order a bite to eat? I don't know about you but I'm famished.'

Dear? Dear? Christ. I really feel like a child sitting here. Oh but what the hell. Christmas is the time when you're supposed to be charitable isn't it, and this can be my good deed of the day. Well, of the year more like, but he seems like a sweet old man and maybe he's just lonely, maybe he just wants some company.

And I am pretty hungry myself, and if we order now I could still make my escape in about an hour's time. Just in time to catch *It's A Wonderful Life* on the box tonight.

I nod my approval, and he signals for the waitress to bring the menus over.

'Goodness,' he says, putting these little half glasses on the end of his nose and peering down at the menu, 'what a choice.'

I have to stifle a giggle because I feel like I'm sitting here with an elderly aunt, and then I think I'm really going to lose it as he starts reading out every single dish.

'Hmmm, corn fed chicken with polenta. Sounds interesting. Grilled loin of tuna with tomato salsa, turkey fritters with cranberry coulis . . .' He just sits there, muttering away to himself, before eventually looking up and asking, 'anything take your fancy, Nina?'

'I'm torn between the chicken and the venison sausages with creamed potatoes.'

If I'm not mistaken a look of shock crosses his face. 'Oh no, no!' He says vehemently. 'You can't possibly eat venison! Deer are such beautiful creatures, we can't allow that.'

'OK,' I shrug, figuring he must be an animal lover. 'I'll have the chicken.'

'Good, good,' he says, lowering the menu. 'And I'll have the turkey fritters.'

'Turkeys, I take it, are not beautiful creatures then?' I smile, to soften the caustic tone in my voice.

'Personally I find turkeys quite frightful,' he smiles, those eyes still twinkling away. 'They deserve to be gobbled up.'

And then a funny thing happens. As he sits there beaming away, I suddenly think that I've met him before. But of course it's ridiculous, because whilst I don't consider myself ageist, as in, I have friends from twenty-five up to forty-five, I don't mix socially with anyone as old as him. But there is, nevertheless, something very familiar about him, only I'm not too sure what it is.

'We wouldn't have met somewhere before would we?' I finally say haltingly.

'Well, yes, we might well have done,' he says mysteriously.

'It's just that you look familiar. Where might we have met?'

'I do an awful lot of travelling around this time of year,' he smiles. 'And I meet many, many people on my travels, so perhaps we've passed, like ships, in the night.'

The only place I've travelled at Christmas is to the corner shop and back to refill stocks of booze and crisps, so somehow I think it highly unlikely that we would have met somewhere exotic, but I let it pass.

I'm about to ask him why he joined the dating agency, when he folds his hands on the table and looks me in the eye.

'Now then Nina. Christmas is a very important time of year, and I've got a feeling that you haven't asked for anything yet for Christmas. Am I right?'

Well yes, actually, he is right, but that's only because there's really very little point. I know exactly what I'll be getting for Christmas, which is exactly what I get for Christmas every year. My mother will buy me a bottle of Chanel no. 5, which I stopped wearing when I was twenty-one, but somehow she still believes it's the exact thing I want, *every* year. My father will give me book vouchers. My Grandma will buy me a pair of polyester pyjamas that are supposed to look like silk, but don't, and my Auntie Judith will buy me smelly things for the bath.

Not exactly a result, I think you'll agree.

'I know what my presents will be,' I say, rolling my eyes, 'so no, there isn't anything I've asked for specifically. There wouldn't be any point.'

'But Nina,' he says, shaking his head sadly. 'It's Christmas, and whilst you might not get exactly what you're looking for, it's the time of year when you have the chance to look back on the year. You can reflect on who you are, where you've come from, where you're going. And sometimes funny things do happen at Christmas, sometimes we get exactly what it is that we want. So come now, Nina, there must be something you want.'

He's looking at me quizzically, and I suddenly feel this great need to tell him what I want, but as I sit there I'm thinking of a million things I'd want, and I don't know where to start.

I want a Porsche Boxter, for starters. I want to have enough money to never have to worry about my overdraft ever again. I want a flat with a garden and an off-street parking space. God, listen to me, I sound so superficial! OK, I also want world peace; I want there to be enough food to go around, with no more starving people in far corners of the world that I'd never go to but occasionally see on television.

'Nina?' He brings me out of my reverie. 'What is it that you really, really want?'

I nearly say, 'to be a Spice girl?' (and for your information, I'd be Difficult Spice), but of course I stop myself, because that would be plain rude, plus the fact that he's so old he probably wouldn't know who the Spice Girls are.

'Forgive me,' he says, with a chuckle. 'I sound like a Spice Girl.'

I look at him in amazement.

'You know who the Spice Girls are?'

He chuckles. 'I seem to be exporting a lot of Spice Girls merchandise this year.'

Now I'm impressed.

'So what is it that you want Nina?'

'Well,' I venture, pausing as our food arrives. 'I think what I'd really like is to be happy.'

'And is there any one thing that would make you happy?' He takes a big bite of turkey fritter and sits looking at me while I think that yes, actually, there are a number of things that would make me happy.

All of the above, plus of course, falling in love with someone who loves me equally in return. That, above all else, would make me very happy indeed, but just as I'm about to say that, I stop, because it suddenly seems very important that I get this right. That I ask for the one thing that really would make me happy, and would having a boyfriend do that for me? I mean, is it really fair to depend on someone else for your happiness? Wouldn't I be bound to be constantly disappointed if I do what I've always done and expected another person to fulfill my every need?

And as I sit there, I realise that I'd be lying if I said it was a man, and although being happy is the one thing I really want, I think I'd quite like to try and be happy on my own. And maybe then, I'd be ready to welcome someone else into my life. God, listen to me. I sound like someone who's just come out of six years of therapy. And so I tell him that.

Nick grins delightedly, and then starts chuckling, and before long the chuckling becomes huge great heaving gulps of laughter, and this guy has the strangest laugh I've ever heard. Seriously. He doesn't laugh like normal people. Nope. He's sitting rocking back and forth on his chair while I pray that no one's watching me and wondering what on earth I'm doing with him, and he's actually saying, 'ho, ho, ho.'

Can you believe it? I'm so shocked I just sit and watch him open-mouthed, because of course I know exactly who he reminds me of, with his little hands tucked round his big fat belly, and his white beard, and, oh my God, his nose actually appears to be reddening.

'Nina dear,' he says finally, recovering his composure, and putting some money on the table for the bill, before reaching over to pick up his coat – and why am I not surprised it's pillarbox red and trimmed with white fur – 'I suspect you will get your wish. Now I must go. Things to do, people to see, goods to export,' and with that he winks.

And just as he leaves he turns to me and covers my hand with his own. 'One more thing, my dear. I don't wish to be the bearer of bad news, but I think you're old enough now to know the truth. There are no such things as knights in shining armour.'

Jane Green's the author of *Straight Talking*,
published by Mandarin.

37

John Hegley

THESE WERE YOUR FATHER'S

CHRISTMAS POETRY

ONE CHRISTMAS my father gave me and my sister a sheet of brown paper each for our main present and said that this year we could enjoy the greatest gift of all – the imagination.

'Children,' he said cheerily, 'these are your magic carpets.'

'But dad,' I complained, 'I wanted a sheet of brown paper.'

'And I wanted a wrapped up present,' complained my sister.

'But this present is its own wrapping paper,' said our father, confusing her rather.

'But she wanted a jigsaw, dad,' I added.

'Well, tear it into pieces then,' added dad in his turn. 'USE those imaginations or I'm going to get annoyed!'

And when he had gone we each imagined the other person's brown paper to be unacceptably bigger and browner than our own.

CHRISTMAS

there came three wise men from the East
and so it came to pass
the wise men found the shepherds
a bit working class

CHRISTMAS WITH THE
BROTHER-IN-LAW (OH WHAT FUN)

the two clip-on earrings slip from our
    Christmas cracker
you can have them John
my brother-in-law quips
I slip into the earrings
how do I look then handsome?
I lie to him
all right John very sexy take them off
he says trying to sound normal in his
    torn Christmas hat
that is sat around his neck
you're not a woman
he reminds me
how do you explain these then?
I reply ripping open my shirt and
    squirting my nipples at him
shall I take these off too?
don't spoil the Christmas John
my mother interrupts

John Hegley's *Family Pack*
is published by Methuen

39

Nicholas Allan

CHRISTMAS KNICKERS

The ultimate Christmas fantasy knickers of Ftion, friend of William Haque

I ♥ the Prime Minister!

To Damien Hirst's

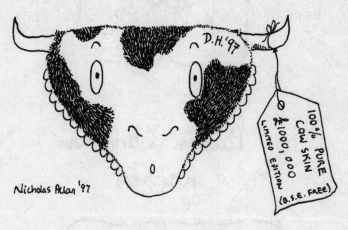

Nicholas Allan '97

100% PURE COW SKIN
£1000,000
LIMITED EDITION
(B.S.E. FREE)

... from and by the artist

41

Liam's   Christmas

Boxers

Patsy's Christmas

Knickers

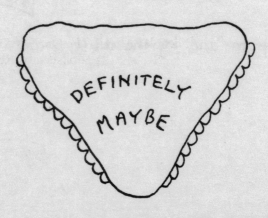

To Madonna...

Like a Virgin

Hanky Spanky

Environmental knickers
with elastic attachment
so when thrown to audience
may be instantly retrievable

Nicholas Allan's *The Queen's Knickers*
is published by Red Fox.

Stephen Fry

THE ADVENTURE OF THE LAUGHING JARVEY

THE FOLLOWING appeared in the Christmas 1987 issue of
The Listener:

> The literary editor, when clearing out her office preparatory to
> the move to *The Listener*'s new quarters, discovered a bundle
> of papers wedged at the back of a drawer. The find appeared
> to be an autograph manuscript of a previously unpublished
> Sherlock Holmes story. Uncertain of its authenticity, she asked
> Stephen Fry, a noted Sherlockian, to edit the text and reflect
> on its provenance.

Hand-written on nineteenth-century foolscap the document
certainly appears to be genuine. According to Edinburgh
University's pioneering 'particle method' a quick count of
prepositions, final clauses and image clusters tells us that the
balance of probability is that the text was indeed written by
Watson. Three or four strange inconsistencies, however,
which do not become apparent until the very end of the story,
throw some doubt on this conclusion. Alert readers will detect
these anomalies and draw their own inferences. Apart from
trimming back the typically profuse growth of commas and
semi-colons familiar to scholars of the canon, I have left the
body of the text unedited. I should be interested to hear the
opinion of enthusiasts everywhere. In my view, if the story is
not genuine then it ought to be.

The year 18— saw my friend Sherlock Holmes at the very height of his considerable powers. On leafing through the journals for that year my attention is caught by a number of cases; some startling, some macabre, some seemingly commonplace, but all demonstrating to a great extent Holmes's remarkable gifts of deduction. The Affair of the Stranded Macaw, for which he received the Order of the Silver Myrtle from the hands of His Majesty the King Miroslaw himself, presents several peculiar features of interest but in the more delicate of its details touches too many figures in public life to allow me to retell it here. The Tale of the Punctual Railway Clerk, while remaining one of Holmes's favourite triumphs, is perhaps of too technical a nature to be of interest to the general reader. The Case of the Copper Beeches I have chronicled elsewhere and the Story of the Tooting Schoolmaster and the Harness, while displaying as perhaps no other the extraordinary meticulousness and patience that characterised my friend's methods, has no place outside specialist journals.

Towards the very end of that year however, when it seemed to us that London had given up on sensation for the winter and was content to prepare itself comfortably for the festive season without throwing up those *outré* mysteries that were as oxygen to Sherlock Holmes, there exploded upon us a case which wrenched him from the indolence and melancholy to which that great mind was prey when there was nothing to engage it and hurtled us into as extraordinary an adventure as any we had known. Although it is his oft repeated assertion that this problem tested his reasoning powers only to the smallest degree, there can be no doubt that its solution yielded to Holmes the richest fee he ever earned in the course of an illustrious career.

I remember that one evening in mid-December I was engaged in the task of decorating our bachelor lodgings with some seasonal sprigs of holly and mistletoe, enduring the while some tart criticisms from my friend.

'Really Watson,' said he, 'is it not enough that Mrs Hudson must come in laden with mince pies and indefatigable good cheer every hour of the day? Must we also deck ourselves out like a pagan temple?'

'I must say, Holmes,' I returned with some asperity, for the effort of standing upon a chair and reaching for the picture rail was taking its toll on the old Jezail bullet wound, 'I think this uncommonly poor-spirited of you! Christmas used to mean something, I remember. Do you not recall the Blue Carbuncle? *That* adventure saw you as full of Yuletide charity as any man.'

'Watson you are confusing the real facts of that affair with the gaudy version of it that you were pleased to set down before a gullible public. Pray do not start upon the course of believing your own fictions. As I remember it, the case was a matter for calm analysis.'

'Really, Holmes,' I ejaculated, 'you are most unfair!'

'You must forgive me Watson. But the infernal *dullness* of it all! A spreading canker of bumbling good cheer seems to infect everybody at this time of year, even the most hardened of scoundrels, who are as likely to give money as they are to abstract it. Here is the *Evening News*. What foul murders or daring larcenies are there here to engage the interest? A woman is injured in a derailment at Lewisham, someone has stolen a statue from Charing Cross, a horse has bolted in Hoxton. I despair, Watson. Let us have an end to this sickening season of good will and peace, I say.'

'Holmes, I will not allow this assault on Christmas! You know perfectly well that –'

But my strictures were interrupted by a wild jangling of the bell downstairs.

'Ah,' said Holmes, 'I am spared your homily. Perhaps a mistaken address, perhaps a client. Such extravagant pealing denotes some urgency at any rate. Well, Billy?'

Our honest pageboy had entered the room, but before he had time to make any formal announcement there burst in like a tornado the most wildly agitated man I think I have ever laid eyes upon.

'Mr Sherlock Holmes? Which one of you is Mr Holmes?' gasped the unfortunate creature, looking wildly from one to the other of us.

'I am he,' said Holmes, 'and this is my friend Dr Watson. If you will be seated he will pour you a glass of brandy.'

'Thank you, a little brandy, yes indeed. That would be most
. . . really Mr Holmes, you must forgive me, I am not given to
. . . thank you, most kind, no seltzer I beg! Just so. Let me
catch my breath . . . splendid rooms, most snug. Charming
holly . . . so festive. I congratulate you. Ah! that is much
better, I am obliged to you, Doctor.'

Despite the pitiable distress of the man I could not forbear
to smile at this twittering and inconsequential monologue. I
had seen physical pain induce such loquacity and delirium in
wounded men and knew it to be a common sign of mental
anxiety also.

Sherlock Holmes sat deep in his armchair, touching
together the tips of his fingers and running an expert eye over
the extraordinary gentleman seated opposite him. Our visitor
was dressed fashionably for the evening, but I could not set
him down as a Society figure. Prosperity gleamed in the
refulgent shirt and hand-made boots, for all the fresh traces of
mud upon them, but too lively an intelligence shone in his
piercingly blue eyes to suppose that he did not use his brain
for a living. His thin face, in its rare moments of repose,
seemed of a melancholy cast, but when it became animated
the features fairly quivered with movement, a wiry beard
wagged and jerked in time to his speech and the wild,
disordered locks upon his head tossed about as if in a tempest.

'Such *very* good brandy . . . oh dear, oh dear, oh dear.
Whatever am I to do, Mr Holmes?'

'Well, when you have caught your breath, you had better
lay your problem before us,' said Holmes. 'To have come
from at least as far as Gray's Inn all the way to Baker Street
on such a night would take its toll on any man.'

Our visitor started visibly. 'But how on earth? Oh dear me,
that is most extraordinary! I have indeed run all the way from
Gray's Inn, though how you could know that is beyond me.'

'Tush, sir, it is as clear as day. That you have been running
a child could tell from your breathlessness alone. The line of
the splashes upon the toes of your boots could not be caused
any other way.'

'Well,' chuckled the other, momentarily diverted from the cause of his peculiar worry, 'I see that, but how the deuce can you read Gray's Inn in my appearance?'

'I was there this morning,' said Holmes. 'They are painting the iron railings that fence off the north side from the pavement. The palings themselves are painted black, but the tip is gilded, in your hurry you have brushed your left arm against the wet paint. See upon your sleeve, black topped with a smudge of gold. It is possible that there is another railing freshly painted in like manner somewhere in London, but it is highly unlikely.'

'Remarkable, remarkable. A capital game! What else, sir? What else?'

'I am afraid,' said Holmes, 'there is very little else to tell.'

'Ah, I am freshly changed into my evening clothes, after all. Every clue starched over, I fancy.'

'Beyond the obvious facts that you are a writer, that you suffered deprivation in your boyhood, that money is a little harder to come by for you than it once was and that you are fond of conjuring tricks, there is certainly very little to be seen,' said Holmes.

Our visitor started up. 'You know me then! This is a pretty trick to play, sir, upon my word! It is unworthy of you.'

'Be seated, I beg,' said Holmes, 'I have never set eyes upon you before. When I see a man with so pronounced an indentation upon the inside of his middle finger it is surely no great matter to assume that he is a writer?'

'A clerk! I might be a clerk!'

'In Lobb boots? I hardly think so.'

'Hum, the deprivation then?'

'Your face is lined beyond your years, but not, I perceive, by the trouble that has brought you here. That is too recent to have yet written itself across your brow. I have seen such marks only on those who grew up knowing misery and want.'

'True enough, Mr Holmes but the money, the conjuring tricks?'

'Those fine boots were made some three or four years ago, I fancy. The excellently cut coat you are wearing dates from that time also. The sudden burst of prosperity that their purchase betokens has receded a little into the past, therefore. As for the conjuring, you will have noticed, I am sure, Watson, the small metal cone that protrudes a little from our visitor's waistcoat? Flesh-pink in colour, it is called a thumb-tip: an essential part of an illusionist's apparatus.'

'Bravo, Mr Holmes!' cried our guest, applauding with great energy. 'Miraculous!'

'Meretricious.'

'And a happy new year, my dear sir. Meretricious and a happy new year! Dear me,' said he, sinking in spirits once more, 'you quite take my mind from the purpose of this visit. Such a calamity, Mr Holmes. Such a dreadful calamity. I am beside myself!'

'I am all attention Mr – ?'

'Oh! My name? Yes. Ah, Bosney, Culliford Bosney, novelist. You have heard of me perhaps?' He scanned our bookshelves eagerly.

'I am afraid, Mr Bosney, that with only a few exceptions I do not have much time for novels. Dr Watson is the literary man.'

Culliford Bosney turned his lively gaze upon me. 'Ah yes, Dr Watson – of course. I read your works with great interest. Accept the compliments of a fellow scribbler, I beg.'

'Thank you,' said I, 'I am afraid Mr Holmes does not share your good opinion of my efforts.'

'Nonsense, Watson! As exotic romances they stand in a class of their own,' said Holmes, filling his briar.

'You see what I have to contend with, Mr Bosney?' said I, with a rueful grin.

'Oh, Dr Watson!' answered he, with a pitiable return to his former woe. 'You will understand my misery when I tell you that it is lost! It is lost, and I am at my wits' end!'

'What is lost?' I asked in bewilderment.

'The manuscript, of course! It is lost and I am sure I shall lose my mind with worrying over it.'

'I think,' said Holmes, leaning back in his chair, 'that you had better favour us with all the facts of your narrative, Mr Bosney.'

'Of course, Mr Holmes. Omitting no details, however trivial they may seem, eh?'

'Quite so.'

'Well, you must know that I have been labouring now for some six weeks on the manuscript of a story. I was due today to deliver it to my publishers – it is necessary that they publish it within the week you understand, for it has a Yuletide theme. I have high hopes for this story, Mr Holmes. I will not palter with you, my last novel did not take at all well and I have been at great pains to do something which will in some way recoup my fortunes and restore the good opinion of the reading public. I have not been on the best of terms with my publishers for some time and I am hoping that this newest work will earn me enough by way of royalties to enable me to leave them and seek a more congenial firm.'

'Are they aware of this ambition?' asked Holmes.

'No, Mr Holmes, I do not believe that they are. I have great hopes of this story however. *Had* great hopes, for I am sure I shall never see it again!' The agonised novelist sprang up from his seat with a gesture of despair. 'Mr Holmes, it is useless. How can one find a needle in a haystack?'

'Given a strong enough magnet, Mr Bosney, it is an elementary task. Put me in possession of the relevant facts and who knows but that we will not be able to find just such a magnet?'

'Yes, yes. I must beg your pardon gentlemen, but I have been tried these past few hours, sorely tried. Well then, at half past four this afternoon I had finished reading the story back to myself and was satisfied that it was ready to be printed. Rather than have the manuscript collected I thought that I would deliver it myself, on my way to the theatre. I also wanted to give some last-minute instructions for the printing. I wished the book to be lavishly presented, Mr Holmes, in gilt and red. I thought that would be appropriately festive.

'I changed into evening clothes, tucked the manuscript under my arm and went out into the street to hail a cab. My street runs into Theobald's Road, Mr Holmes, just opposite Gray's Inn. There is usually no difficulty in finding a hackney carriage on that thoroughfare. To my surprise, however, there was already a hansom standing right outside my house. I called to the driver to ask if he were waiting for anybody. He seemed startled but replied that he was not. I opened the door, put the manuscript on to the seat and was on the point of climbing in, when I noticed that the seat was already occupied. Mr Holmes, I am not a fanciful man, but the sight of the figure sitting in the corner of that hansom made my blood run cold! A deathly pale countenance, with blank unseeing eyes. I shudder at the memory of him.'

'You recollect how the figure was dressed?' asked Holmes sharply.

'I do indeed, it was most striking. I recall a many-caped driving coat buttoned up to the throat, a billycock hat and a woollen scarf. There was something so incongruous about this strange apparel and those inhumanly blanched and spectral features that I could not help but step backwards with a cry. No sooner had I done so than the jarvey whipped up his horse with a shout and rattled down the street, disappearing into the mist.'

'Really?' said Holmes, rubbing his hands together. 'Most intriguing. Pray continue, Mr Bosney, I beg.'

'I must own, Mr Holmes, that I was at first relieved that the vision had fled so fast. I stood trembling upon the pavement, wondering at the meaning of so horrid a sight. Perhaps I had imagined it, perhaps I was still in the grip of the fever of imagination with which I had finished my story. But then I remembered that my manuscript was still lying on the seat of the vanished cab and I became quite mad with fright. I ran down into Theobald's Road and stared about me. There were dog-carts and broughams and hansoms by the dozen rattling in both directions. But which was my hansom, I could not tell. I have sent my servants out to the cab companies offering large rewards for the safe return of the manuscript Mr Holmes, but so far with no success. I am at my wits' end!'

'A piquant mystery,' said Holmes, looking dreamily up at the ceiling. 'Can you describe the jarvey to me, I wonder?'

'I cannot Mr Holmes!' groaned the other. 'I usually have an

excellent memory for faces, but this man was so muffled up against the chill that I had no opportunity to read his features. I have an impression from his voice that he was a young man, but I may be wrong. Also –'

'Yes?'

'Well, it may only be my fancy, but I could swear that as the cab hurtled away from me I heard laughter. I attributed it to the medical students who have just moved in to lodgings next door to me and are rowdy at the best of times, but thinking back I am sure it came from the jarvey himself! What can that mean, Mr Holmes?'

'A laugh you say? Now, that is really most revealing.' Holmes rose and began to pace about the room. 'You have mentioned students, Mr Bosney, what other neighbours do you have?'

'For the most part we are a quiet lot – solicitors and stockbrokers in the main. The street is handy for both the Inns of Court and the City of London. I am not on especially intimate terms with any of my neighbours, however. Colonel Harker, whose house adjoins mine, has recently returned from India and staffs his household with native servants, at whom he bellows with immoderate choler. I do not think that I have ever exchanged above two words with him. He is away in Hampshire for Christmas in any case, so I do not think he can have any bearing on the matter.'

'Well, Mr Bosney,' said Holmes, buttoning up his cape, 'I will look into this little problem for you.'

'Thank you, Mr Holmes!'

'Come Watson, let us all take ourselves to Gray's Inn and see what we can discover.'

*

As the three of us were whisked through the dark London streets, Sherlock Holmes and Culliford Bosney looked out the window at the fog-wrapped streets and alleyways of the great capital, the former keenly, the latter with comical anxiety. Holmes, drawing heavily on his most pungent shag mixture, noted off the street names as we flew down the Euston Road. I have remarked before that his knowledge of London streets was profound, from the lowest and vilest alleys in the east to the broadest and most fashionable squares and avenues in the west. I was surprised to discover that Mr Bosney too was possessed of an exact acquaintance with the capital. The pair of them talked enthusiastically of their love for the great city, Bosney even contriving to surprise Holmes on occasion with some obscure fragment of history or local anecdote.

'Yes indeed, Mr Holmes!' cried he, 'London is alive, believe me. Every citizen is like a cell of the great organism, connected to every other. The meanest tapster in Limehouse and the grandest duke in Grosvenor Square are bound together and give life each to each! You think me fanciful perhaps?'

'Not at all, sir,' replied Holmes, 'my work largely depends upon that fact. What is a crime but a disease? My work is largely diagnostic: just as Watson here might see a deficiency of iron in a swollen elbow, so I might detect a suburban murder in a frayed cuff. A death in Houndsditch may leave the inhabitants of Belgravia unmoved, but they mistake the matter if they do not believe themselves involved.'

'Mr Holmes, you are a man after my own heart,' said Bosney warmly. 'And is this not the season for just such reflections?'

'As to that, Mr Bosney,' said Holmes with a wry look towards me, 'I must confess that what with the weather on the one hand and the false civilities on the other, Christmas leaves me quite cold.'

'Why then,' returned the other in some surprise, 'you are a perfect – ah, here is Gray's Inn. See how they have now put up signs warning the unwary of the fresh paint upon the palings. Good cheer, Tom!' This last remark was addressed to a young crossing-sweeper who had stepped smartly up to open the door for us as we drew up, and to whom Bosney tossed some pennies.

My heart sank as I looked at the tide of traffic roaring past us and crossing the Gray's Inn Road. How could Holmes hope to recover one lost bundle of papers in such a vast confusion of humanity?

As always when Sherlock Holmes was engaged on a case, his reflective lassitude gave way to an extraordinary vigour and his demeanour took on the keen expression of a greyhound loosed from the slips.

'This is your street down here, I take it?' he inquired of our companion. 'John's Street, I think it is called.'

'Exactly so, I inhabit one of the houses further down, where it changes its name before joining Guildford Street,' replied Mr Bosney, scampering to keep up with Holmes as he strode down the well-lit thoroughfare. 'Here we are, allow me to invite you in for some warming negus, I beg.'

'Thank you. Later perhaps. Now the cab stood here, I perceive? Quite so. No rain has fallen this afternoon, that is good.'

Holmes whipped out his lens, dropped onto all fours and began to scramble about on the ground outside Culliford Bosney's house. To one so well acquainted with Sherlock Holmes and his methods, the minuteness of the scrutiny and the animal energy with which he conducted it held no real surprises for me, but the novelist watched with frank astonishment as Holmes, with blithe disregard for the knees of his trousers, crawled in the mud of the cobbled kerbside, now scooping tiny objects into a fold of paper produced from an inside pocket, now measuring invisible marks upon the ground with a tape.

At last, Holmes rose to his feet. 'Now, Mr Bosney, this house here that adjoins yours, this belongs to the Colonel from India, or to the medical students?'

'To the students. That house there, all shut up, is Colonel Harker's.'

'As I assumed. We must make haste if we are to recover your manuscript. I think now I will go into the house.'

I followed Mr Bosney to his front door, but turned in surprise to see Holmes proceeding down the front path of the neighbouring house.

'Why Holmes!' I cried, 'this is the house.'

'On the contrary Watson. You were a medical student once, you should be aware that *this* is the house.' So saying he pulled at the doorbell. 'Read the ground, gentlemen, it is the skin of the great organism we were discussing and bears battlescars that can testify to many a strange history.' The door opened and a maid admitted Holmes into the dwelling.

'Well!' said Mr Bosney. 'Most extraordinary! What can these students have to do with the matter?'

'I think we should wait,' said I, 'Holmes very rarely makes a mistake. If he thinks that they have some connection with the mystery, then you may depend upon it that they have. Come, let us look at the ground and see if we cannot follow his reasoning.'

The pair of us spent a fruitless quarter of an hour examining the mud of the street with the aid of a lens that Bosney brought out from his house. Whatever code was printed there was too cryptic for us to decipher, however, and we were just climbing the steps of Mr Bosney's house to partake of a hot posset when the door of the students' lodgings opened and a young man shot out, clutching a hat to his head and running at breakneck speed down the street. He was followed a few moments later by Sherlock Holmes, who eyed the retreating figure with benevolent amusement.

'An elementary problem, Mr Bosney. Appropriately frivolous for the time of year. If you would be so good as to return with us to Baker Street, I think I may be able to shed a little light on the matter.'

'But . . . but Mr Holmes!' cried the other. 'The manuscript! You mean you have found it?'

'Unless we are very unfortunate, it should be in your hands within the hour.'

*

Not a word would Holmes vouchsafe us, on our homeward journey, save the observation that were all cases as simple as this one, life would soon become insupportably dull.

When we were ensconced in the comfortable warmth of 221B Baker Street, Holmes plucked a book from the shelves and left Culliford Bosney and I to complete the festive decoration of the rooms while he read. Of a sudden, Holmes closed his book with a laugh.

'Well, Watson, perhaps this will turn out to be a case for your memoirs after all. Most remarkable. I should have known, of course.'

'What should you have known, Holmes?' we cried in exasperation.

'We were remarking earlier, Mr Culliford Bosney,' said Sherlock Holmes, with an uncharacteristic twinkle, 'that all things in this great capital interconnect in surprising ways. The observers of life, such as ourselves, must place ourselves like spiders at the centre of the great web, and train ourselves to interpret every twitch upon the gossamer, every tremble of the fibre. As soon as you mentioned to me that you lived next door to medical students I registered just such a quiver on the web. Perhaps it meant something, perhaps nothing, but I filed it away just the same. Watson may remember my remarking that the only notable crime London had to offer today was the removal of a statue from Charing Cross. You may be aware, Mr Bosney, that it is the habit of medical students to play pranks upon each other. The rivalry between the students of the two great hospitals at Charing Cross and Guy's is legendary.'

'Why, that's true!' I cried, 'I remember in my day that we –'

'Quite,' said Holmes, always impatient of interruption. 'I had therefore already set down in my mind the theft of the statue as an incident of just such festive exuberance. Your mention of medical students, Mr Bosney, while conceivably immaterial, prepared me for some connection. As soon as I came upon the scene of your meeting with the spectral hansom the true facts of the matter became clear to me. To the trained eye the tracks in the kerbside were easy enough to interpret. I saw at once that the cab had been waiting outside the *students'* house, Mr Bosney, not your own. The signs of movement and restlessness on the part of the horse also told me that no professional London jarvey had been at the reins. It had been all the driver could do to keep the horse still while the statue was loaded into the cab.'

'A statue!' Culliford Bosney clapped his hands together. 'Of course! The awful fixed stare and the ghostly pallor!'

'You were an excellent witness, Mr Bosney, but you failed to interpret your own evidence. Your senses had already told you that you beheld something inhuman, but you refused to make the logical inference.'

'Ghosts were much on my mind, Mr Holmes. I had after all just completed a fiction and was perhaps still dwelling in the world of the imagination. But what of the manuscript?'

'I called on the students, as you observed. They were most communicative. They revealed to me that for the purposes of the jape one of their number had hired a hansom for the day and bribed the cabbie to stay away. He had purloined the statue and brought it straight to your street, Mr Bosney. There the other students came out and dressed it up. I already knew that something of the sort had taken place from the disposition of footprints outside. The students had then gone back into the house, leaving their ringleader in charge of the cab, while they changed into builders' overalls. It was their mad intention to climb Temple Bar and place the statue in a prominent position overlooking the traffic. The young gentleman who had played the part of the cabbie related to me how you had accosted him while his friends were still inside. You took him so by surprise when you hailed him, that he did not think to say that he was engaged.'

'The young hound!' exclaimed Culliford Bosney.

'He is most penitent I assure you,' said Holmes. 'I think I may say without conceit that he was a little startled to find Sherlock Holmes on his trail.'

'A hammer to crack a nut, to be sure . . . but the manuscript, Mr Holmes?'

'Ah the manuscript! Your cabbie took advantage of the moment when you sprung back in amazement from the cab to make good his escape. He contrived to smuggle the statue into Charing Cross Hospital itself and put it into a bed where, as far as he knows, it remains still. He returned the hansom to the cab company who had hired it out to him and had reached his lodgings next door to your house not half an hour before we arrived upon the scene. He has a vague memory of seeing a bundle of papers in the back of the cab, but he paid them no attention. When I made it plain to him that the loss of that manuscript would result in the story of his adventures being made known to the dean of his hospital he rushed from the house to recover it. I think I hear his tread upon the stair now.'

Just at that moment the door opened to admit a flushed young man carrying a large bundle of papers.

'My manuscript!' cried Mr Bosney, leaping to his feet.

'Allow me to present Mr Jasper Corrigan,' said Holmes. 'This is my good friend Dr Watson, and this gentleman, whose manuscript you appear to have found, is your neighbour, the novelist.'

'Well sir, I believe I owe you an apology,' said the medical student, holding out a hand. 'I'm sure Mr Holmes here has told you everything. Believe me when I say that I had no intention of doing you such a wrong.'

'My dear fellow,' said Mr Bosney, warmly shaking hands, 'think nothing of it! If the manuscript is complete . . . let me see . . .' He took the bundle of papers and examined them eagerly. 'Yes, it is all here. I will take it to the printers this instant. Will they be open at this time of the evening? But they have a night staff. Yes, this very instant! Mr Corrigan, I hope you will do me the honour of coming with your friends to my house tomorrow night. We shall have a party! Yes, with chestnuts and games and all manner of fun. A man should know his neighbours. It is disgraceful that I have not invited you before. Marshmallows too, and a hot punch! Please tell me you will come.'

'Sir, we should be honoured. We . . . I do not deserve such generosity.'

'Pooh! Is it not Christmas? As for you, Mr Holmes, I am sure I do not know where to begin . . . such brilliance, such –'

'Really, Mr Bosney, you are too kind,' said Holmes, smiling a little at the author's exuberance. 'I am happy that your story is saved, but I think on reflection that you will see that it was not a testing problem. Indeed it is probable that it would have solved itself without my aid.'

'That I cannot allow,' replied Mr Bosney, 'I insist that you name your fee.'

'As to that,' said Holmes, 'I *will* ask a fee from you.'

'Name it, Mr Holmes, name it!'

'I have a fancy to own that manuscript of yours. When it returns from the printers, I wonder if you will send it to me?'

Mr Bosney blinked slightly. 'Really Mr Holmes, you do me a great honour. You told me you have no time for fiction.'

'Some fiction I have all the time in the world for, Mr Bosney, and I have an idea that I will enjoy your story. I think it is you who are doing me the honour.'

'Shake my hand, sir!' said the other. 'You are a remarkable man. A remarkable man.'

*

Mr Bosney was as good as his word and the manuscript arrived a week later through the post. Holmes took it up immediately and for the next two hours sat reading it. When he had finished, he looked up and I saw that there were tears in his eyes.

'Really Watson,' he said at last. 'Couldn't we have more holly about the place? It is Christmas, you know.'

'But Holmes!' I expostulated.

'Read it, Watson,' he said passing the manuscript over to me. 'Just read it.'

I took it up and looked at the cover page. 'But . . . but . . . Holmes!'

'Quite, Watson.'

I looked at the manuscript again. On the cover page was written, 'A Christmas Carol, by Charles Culliford Boz Dickens.'

'And a merry Christmas to us all!' said Holmes.

Stephen Fry is the author of several novels. His autobiography, *Moab is my Washpot*, is published by Hutchinson.

Monty Python

THE LIFE OF BRIAN
(of Nazareth)

THE NIGHT SKY. *Three camels are silhouetted against the bright stars of the moonless sky, moving slowly along the horizon. A star leads them towards* BETHLEHEM.

The WISE MEN *enter the gates of the sleeping town and make their way through the deserted streets. A dog snarls at them. They approach a lighted stable, light streams out. Dismounting and entering they find a typical manger scene, with a baby in a rough crib of straw, patient animals standing around. The mother nods by the side of the child. Suddenly she wakes from her lightish doze, sees them, shrieks and falls backwards off her straw. She's up again in a flash, looking guardedly at them. She is a ratbag.*

MANDY: Who are you?

FIRST WISE MAN: We are three wise men.

THIRD WISE MAN: We are astrologers. We have come from the East.

MANDY: Is this some kind joke?

FIRST WISE MAN: We wish to praise the infant.

SECOND WISE MAN: We must pay homage to him.

MANDY: Homage!! You're all drunk you are. It's disgusting. Out, out.

THIRD WISE MAN: No, no.

MANDY: Coming bursting in here first thing in the morning with some tale about Oriental fortune tellers . . . get out.

FIRST WISE MAN: No. No we must see him.

MANDY: Go and praise someone else's brat, go on.

SECOND WISE MAN: We were led by a star.

MANDY: Led by a bottle, more like. Get out!

60

SECOND WISE MAN: We must see him. We have brought presents.

MANDY: Out.

FIRST WISE MAN: Gold, frankincense, myrrh.

[MANDY *changes direction, smooth as silk*.]

MANDY: Well, why didn't you say? He's over here . . . Sorry this place is a bit of a mess. What is myrrh, anyway?

THIRD WISE MAN: It is a valuable balm.

MANDY: A balm, what are you giving him a balm for? It might bite him.

THIRD WISE MAN: What?

MANDY: It's a dangerous animal. Quick, throw it in the trough.

THIRD WISE MAN: No it isn't.

MANDY: Yes it is.

THIRD WISE MAN: No, no, it is an ointment.

MANDY: An ointment?

THIRD WISE MAN: Look.

MANDY [*sampling the ointment with a grubby finger*:] Oh. There is an animal called a balm, or did I dream it? You astrologers, eh? Well, what's he then?

SECOND WISE MAN: H'm?

MANDY: What star sign is he?

SECOND WISE MAN: Capricorn.

MANDY: Capricorn eh, what are they like?

SECOND WISE MAN: He is the son of God, our Messiah.

FIRST WISE MAN: King of the Jews.

MANDY: And that's Capricorn, is it?

THIRD WISE MAN: No, no, that's just him.

MANDY: Oh, I was going to say, otherwise there'd be a lot of them.

[*The* WISE MEN *are on their knees*.]

SECOND WISE MAN: By what name are you calling him?

[*Dramatic chord*.]

MANDY: . . . Brian.

THREE WISE MEN: We worship you, Oh Brian, who are Lord over us all. Praise unto you, Brian and to the Lord our Father. Amen.

MANDY: Do you do a lot of this, then?

FIRST WISE MAN: What?

MANDY: This praising.

FIRST WISE MAN: No, no, no.

MANDY: Oh! Well, if you're dropping by again do pop in.
[*They take the hint and rise.*]

MANDY: And thanks a lot for the gold and frankincense but
. . . don't worry too much about the myrrh next time.
Thank you . . . Goodbye.

MANDY [*to Brian:*] Well weren't they nice . . . out of their
bloody minds, but still . . .

[*In the background we see the* WISE MEN *pause outside
the door as a gentle glow suffuses them. They look at each
other, confer and then stride back in and grab the presents
off* MANDY *and turn to go again, pushing* MANDY *over.*]

MANDY: Here, here, that's mine, you just gave me that. Ow.

[*Cut to exterior* BETHLEHEM *street again. The* WISE MEN
*come out of the stable bathed in a gentle light. They look in
the direction of the light and we pan to reveal the
archetypal manger scene with* MARY, JOSEPH *and the*
INFANT JESUS. *The* WISE MEN *move into shot and kneel.*

Cut back to MANDY *and her brat. It howls.* MANDY
smacks it.]

Main title sequence.

MONTY PYTHON'S LIFE OF BRIAN
[*The music sweeps – desperately.*]
       Brian . . . the babe they called Brian
       Grew . . . grew grew and grew, grew up to be
       A boy called Brian
       A boy called Brian

       He had arms and legs and hands and feet
       This boy whose name was Brian
       And he grew, grew, grew and grew
       Grew up to be
       Yes he grew up to be

A teenager called Brian
A teenager called Brian
And his face became spotty
Yes his face became spotty
And his voice dropped down low
And things started to grow
On young Brian and show
He was certainly no
No girl named Brian
Not a girl named Brian

And he started to shave
And have one off the wrist
And want to see girls
And go out and get pissed
This man called Brian
This man called Brian

Monty Python's *The Life of Brian (of Nazareth)*
is published by Mandarin.

Rolf Harris

BEASTLY BEHAVIOUR

IT WAS CERTAINLY A Christmas to remember for Carmel and Peter Sandham – and for Sandy, their Labrador. As the family settled down to sleep on Christmas Eve at their home in Chadderton, Greater Manchester, Sandy decided that she simply couldn't wait until tomorrow for Christmas dinner. Following her nose, she trotted into the kitchen and proceeded to scoff a 17lb turkey, 2lbs of sausages, 2lbs of prawns, a plate of smoked salmon, 10 rashers of bacon, a pot of apple sauce, all the Paxo and a vast helping of potatoes, carrots, turnips and parsnips. Christmas dinner finished, Sandy's mind immediately turned to dessert. She decided to have 12 ginger and brandy puddings in lemon sauce, a tub of cream and a box of chocolates – just to round things off.

On Christmas morning, Carmel came downstairs to find an extremely bloated Sandy sprawled in the living room looking very pleased with herself and not a scrap of Christmas dinner left. 'I was frantic,' says Carmel. 'But with all the shops closed there was nothing I could do.' The family had to make do with what was left in the fridge – meat pie and chips and no dessert. They couldn't even enjoy the chocolate-filled advent calendar they'd bought. Sandy had eaten that two weeks earlier!

Beastly Behaviour, has just been
published by Century. Rolf Harris's previous book,
True Animal Tales, is available in paperback from Arrow.

Jennifer Paterson

CHRISTMAS PUDDING

1 oz blanched almonds	3 oz soft white breadcrumbs
1 oz glacé cherries	¼ lb chopped suet
2 oz mixed peel	small pinch of salt
¼ lb raisins	large pinch of mixed spice
6 oz currants	small pinch of freshly grated nutmeg
6 oz sultanas	1 small lemon
¼ lb soft brown sugar	2 eggs
3 oz self-raising flour	6 tablespoons barley wine

This is for a 2¼-pint pudding basin.

Put a large pan of water to boil. Wash and dry the fruit unless prewashed. Roughly chop the almonds and cherries. Mix all the fruit and dry ingredients well together with the grated rind and juice of the lemon. Whisk the eggs lightly with the barley wine and stir into the dry ingredients. Mix thoroughly (giving each member of the family a stir for luck); if you are going to put coins in give them a good boil first. When all mixed, turn into a well greased pudding basin. Cut a square of foil (double thickness) two inches wider than the top of the basin. Make a pleat in the middle. Press edges under the rim of the basin, pleating as you go. To facilitate lifting the basin out of the hot water later, cut a double thickness of foil long enough to go under the basin and hang over the saucepan on both sides for handles. Lower the basin into the boiling water which should come threequarters of the way up the basins side. Boil gently for six hours, topping up with boiling water periodically. Remove and cool, cover with more foil and keep until needed. Boil pudding for another two hours before eating.

7 October 1989

Clarissa Dickson Wright and Jennifer Paterson's *Two Fat Ladies* and *Two Fat Ladies Ride Again* are published by Ebury.

Clarissa Dickson Wright

CHRISTMAS

WHEN I WAS A CHILD I thought as a child and my eyes were the eyes of a child and Christmas was very simple. I was raised a Catholic and Christmas was the story of Bethlehem and the stable, the shepherds and so on. From a very early age I was taken to Midnight Mass at a convent of Spanish nuns in Holland Park. We called them the nunnie-buns because they were all very small and rather plump. I remember the strange high singing and that their enthusiasm was also that of a child – they called me Claricita and plied me with strange sweets I didn't much like but ate to join in. After Mass they played guitars and danced Sevillianas and were amazingly happy: it was the only time I ever saw nuns dance. In every Catholic Christmas there is the underlying darkness of the future of Calvary and the Cross but also the shining light of Easter. But in England the older underlying fest of Yule is also always present: the Druidical fight in the darkness of winter when you feast on the reserves of food you should be saving in order to raise morale for the dark days before spring. It is a pledge of trust that spring will come and foodstocks be replenished. Both the tree and the plum pudding are symbols of Yule as surely as the crib and *Adeste Fidelis* stand for Christ in Christmas.

I did not understand all that then, of course, nor did I like Christmas, indeed I dreaded it. I was very much the baby in my family and by the time I was ten the others had all escaped. I use the word advisedly. Privilege is no protector against hatred and alcoholism and whilst it may be a better class of bruise if the poker has an ormolu handle it hurts just as much. My father was a violent and frightening alcoholic and he hated Christmas. Raised as a Plymouth Brethren and an atheist by choice he waged war on the holiday with single handed ferocity. Every Advent he read to me from Charles Dickens *A Christmas Carol*, but I had to wait until I was fourteen and read it for myself to discover it had a happy ending. One year he preserved our much loved budgerigar in formaldehyde for three months so he could conduct its funeral on Christmas morning. The battle over the buying of presents was a war of wits which drove my mother mad. One year when my mother had no money of her own he cancelled all the accounts at various shops. How proud I was when I worked out he wouldn't have closed his account at John Bell & Croyden and everyone got toiletries for Christmas. I was ten years old!

My father was Senior Surgeon at St Marys in Paddington and there was the routine of a hospital Christmas with all its forced jollity. I never understood, and remain sure until this day that if I were too ill to go home, I would rather be left in peace. I did my bit by handing round the turkey – I was a pretty lively child and the patients liked me – and then we went home. There were never any other children in my home at Christmas and all too soon I ceased to see with the eyes of a child.

My dislike of Christmas continued throughout my adult life. America – that inventor of so much that is tasteless – has imposed its own materialism on us. But there is no Christ in Christmas unless we search for it. Even my old headmistress, a Sacred Heart nun, sent me a card with Dolphins last year. Where our Christmas beliefs are now is best summed up by a Japanese Christmas card I once saw and which showed Santa Claus crucified and wishing us all Merry Yule from the Cross!

'Now I see but as through a glass darkly' – any alcoholic will identify with those chilling words and for 12 long years that is what I did. Cooks are in high demand at Christmas time to prepare what is in fact the easiest meal of the year and great acclaim is given to the preparation of this relatively simple feast. Though I do remember that one Christmas dinner when I cooked for a firm of solicitors, the oven in their office kitchen had clearly not been cleaned for years and when I turn it on clouds of black smoke belched forth. I had to clean it before I could start. They all got very drunk waiting and I was there before them. I cooked for many Christmases and bitterly resented it when the families I cooked for insisted that I joined them when I just wanted to be left in peace with my Gin.

Christmas is not a good time for alcoholics: the pubs are full of amateurs pretending they can hold their drink and blocking service at the bar. Money best spent on drink has to be wasted on presents and all the pressures to enjoy yourself are tedious and lead to paranoia. One suspects, probably rightly, that people who do invite you are doing so to feel the warm glow of righteousness and even the extra free drinks are less welcome in the spirit of forced bonhomie.

Ten years ago I found sobriety and in the first flush of enthusiasm took on board all the myths and pressures of Christmas. I tried to celebrate with my family with whom I had nothing in common, even less now that I wasn't drinking. I continued to hate it and hated myself for hating it, and hated myself further for getting out of it. Two years ago I enjoyed Christmas for the first time. I went to stay with my friends, the MacDonalds, on Skye. They own the delightful Kinloch Lodge Hotel which they close at Christmas and restore it to a family home. They are a happy and delightful family and Claire loves Christmas. Her warmth and unbridled enthusiasm sweeps us all along and I feel very privileged to be included. They are Catholics and the crib wins out over America but with a definite inclusion of the lavish hedonism of Yule. This year they are building a church on Skye, appropriately enough in a stable donated by a local resident and we hope it will be open for Midnight Mass.

What conclusions do I draw from all this waffling? That it is possible for a lonely child from a wretched home to enjoy Christmas in middle age. I shall go to Skye and try to keep the balance between Christ and Yule, religion and spirituality in the company of dear friends. Most of all, I will try to see with the eyes of a child, for as Christ says, 'Unless we are as little children we cannot enter the Kingdom of Heaven.'

Clarissa Dickson Wright and Jennifer Paterson's *Two Fat Ladies* and *Two Fat Ladies Ride Again* are published by Ebury.

Jane Gardam

MISS MISTLETOE

DAISY FLAGG WAS A parasite. Nothing wrong with that. Hers is a useful and ancient profession. In Classical times every decent citizen had a parasite. There were triclinia full of them. They flourished throughout Europe in the Middle Ages, though later demoted in England to the status of mere court jesters — demoted because your pure parasite does not have to sing for his supper. Not a bar. Not a note. His function is to sit there smiling below the salt cellar; not ostentatiously below it, but as *ami de maison*.

Now and then the parasite was noticed by those upstream above the salt, among the silver platters. Sometimes he was taunted and had to pretend to enjoy it. There was a Roman parasite who was teased by his host that he had only been invited because the host was having his way with the parasite's wife, and Ha! ha! ha! the parasite had to reply.

Professional parasites turn up even today in Italy – at country weddings, sloping around at the back of the chairs, jollying people along at the wine-feast, nobody knowing who they are. The host sees they get their dinner.

Oh, the parasite was always a self-respecting fellow in his chosen profession. He knew he was easing the host's passage through this world and into the next. He was Lazarus raised up from the city gate. He was the rich man's ticket to heaven.

And there's something of him left still, especially at Christmas-time in England. We've all met him: the friend who's always at the Honeses', the Dishforths', the Hookaneyes'; who provides none of the spread, is no relation, doesn't do a hand's turn, seems to have little rapport with

71

the rest of the company and is not particularly inspiring. Dear Arthur. Jim's friend Alan Something. Dorothy-she-was-something-to-do-with-your-grandmother. Mr Jackson (Beatrix Potter knew all about Mr Jackson). And it is excellent for all, because the host of any one of these people can say, 'And there'll be Mr Jackson of course as usual, God help us. But it *is* Christmas,' and Mr Jackson can say when the drunken invitation is at last extended at the office party on Christmas Eve, 'Oh, thanks, but at Christmas I always go to the Infills.'

And so it was with Daisy Flagg, the Christmas parasite known to the Infills behind her back as Miss Mistletoe. For years and years she had come to the Infills for Christmas, always arriving late following extensive devotions in her parish church some hundred miles away. She drew up in her ancient and decrepit car (which she maintained and serviced, patched and painted herself), its windscreen hazy, its tyres criminally worn, its back seat of rubbed-away, hollowed-out leather laden with awful presents. 'Sorry I'm late,' she would cry, springing through the back door into the kitchen, leaving the car in the middle of the frosty drive below the Renaissance urns on the terrace, all the eighteenth-century windows glittering in disdain. 'Happy Christmas, happy Christmas, all. *Terribly* sorry.' She entered by the kitchen as privileged member of the family, a family that now cooked its own Christmas dinner rather better, if more chaotically, than when there were cooks, and who because of the presence of Daisy Flagg/Miss Mistletoe behaved rather less badly among the bread sauce and the prune stuffing and the whirling machinery that resulted in the brandy butter than they otherwise would have done.

Daisy Flagg/Miss Mistletoe sat to table with her face in its permanent rictus grin, giving the impression of a delighted grasshopper in a paper hat. She was flat as a child, sideways almost invisible, transparent as a pressed flower. She was very clean. Her clothes seemed to have been boiled, her hair almost shampooed away, her nails scrubbed seashells. ('Some sort of guilt there,' said Laetitia the year she was doing Psychology.)

Her shoes came from the jumble sales of her spiky church. They were often the old dancing slippers of dowagers, and once were gigantic Doc Martens found in a paper bag on the pavement in Victoria Street. Miss Mistletoe, who was very poor, had of course taken these straight to the police station. To the very top police station, Scotland Yard, just across the road. They had told here there that lost shoes were not their speciality and if they were her they'd keep them.

Miss Mistletoe wore miniskirts. Always. She must have acquired a great number of them some hot summer in the Beatles' time, for they were all very flimsy and her knees seemed to knock together beneath them in the icy wastes of Infill Hall. Her hair was always done for Christmas in a Cilla Black beehive *circa* 1975. It made her look steady and controlled; the permanent spinster, if the word still exists.

She ate voraciously, keeping the conversation flowing, trooping with the rest out of the dining room to listen to the Queen. She ignored the children. She didn't like children. And she never walked the dogs in the park. Long ago she had been dissuaded from helping with the washing-up, for she tended to hop and giggle and drop the Infill Spode on the flagstones. 'Just sit and be comfortable,' they said, and disappeared with the retrievers into spinneys and woodlands and to trudge round the ornamental lake in the park.

Like a little bundle of sticks sat Miss Mistletoe beside the fire in the hall, across from vast old Archie, bibulous and asleep. She kept up her merry patter – the weather, her car, her journey, the Royal Family (not the sex scandals), *The Archers*, anything. When it was teatime she stayed on. Drinks time, she stayed on. Supper, she stayed on. A sort of pallet had always been laid out for her in a remote bedroom once occupied by a Victorian tubercular tweeny who was said to haunt it, though Miss Mistletoe never complained. Grey blankets and a towel were laid across this bed and these were always left so perfectly folded the next day that everyone wondered if Miss Mistletoe slept in the bed at all. On Christmas night about midnight someone would say, the brandy flowing pretty free by now, though Miss Mistletoe never touched a drop of it, nor alcohol at all: 'Come on, Daisy; you'd better stay the night.' 'Would that be all right?' was the awaited reply. 'It's terribly kind of you.' And she grinned and grinned.

The joke for Boxing Day was how to get rid of her. You couldn't say that everyone was going hunting because nobody did now. The horses were gone and the stables rented out as craft shops and mushroom beds. Laetitia still attended the meet in the village, but in her Lagonda because she was now a hunt saboteur. Nor could you say that everyone was going to the panto in Salisbury, because Miss Mistletoe's face seemed to say to them, 'Why didn't you get a ticket for me?'

Usually they eased her out about noon with the second turkey leg and a wedge of the pudding and a tin of Boots' Lavender talcum powder which had always been her Christmas present. After waving her off they went back into the house and gathered up the presents she had given them and put them with the stuff for the NSPCC summer fair. They shrieked and groaned about Miss Mistletoe for the rest of the day.

Over the years some Infills died and some new ones were born but the numbers for the table at Christmas stayed more or less steady between fourteen and twenty. The year old Archie died, however, spread out peacefully over the logs one November morning early (though they didn't realise it till after *Newsnight*), the numbers had dropped. There would be only twelve, with Miss Mistletoe making the dreaded number of thirteen, and the oft-raised but never seriously considered question began to be asked outright: Do we have to have her?

'We could ask someone else and make it fourteen.'

'Who?'

Nobody could think.

'Well, we can't sit down thirteen. I'm not superstitious but, I mean, Christmas is a religious do. That's when thirteen started.'

'It didn't,' said Laetitia, who was at present concerned with Theology.

'We could say we were all going away.'

'She knows we never go away.'

'Well, we might. We could say we are all going skiing.'

'Don't be silly. Letty and Hubert are over ninety.'

'We could say we're all going on a cruise.'

So they said they were all going on a cruise and they sent Daisy Flagg a fat cheque (ten pounds) and loving messages saying they knew that she would have much more exciting places to go than Infill Hall. Daisy Flagg wrote back on her lined paper in her schoolgirl hand to say it was quite all right, perfectly all right, and she'd be going to a friend in Potter's Bar.

Sighs of relief.

'She's such a *bore*,' they said. 'How many years have we had her? Twenty?'

'Oh no. Not twenty. It feels like twenty. Maybe ten.'

'How old is Daisy Flagg?' someone asked as the turkey was rather wearily dismembered, paper hats lying about the table and not on anybody's head. 'Forty? Fifty?'

'Could be any age. Could be only thirty-five. She was just a little girl in a first job when Mamma found her, wasn't she? Glove counter in the Army & Navy. Took a fancy. Isn't she still there?'

'No idea. I always thought she was something to do with Nannie.'

'Well, we needn't escape all afternoon anyway. Ghastly cold out there.' And they sat about indoors for hours, missing the Queen.

'We can hear her later,' said Jocelyn.

'If we must,' said Laetitia.

But somehow they didn't.

The evening hung heavy. Children fought over videos. Nobody would sit in Archie's splayed chair. The dogs lay around making smells because nobody would take them out. Nobody could face the second turkey leg. 'Next year,' said someone, 'better have the little creature back, don't you think?'

When, the following October, Laetitia decided to go and

75

work for Mother Theresa in Calcutta (calling in at Rome on the way for a new handbag), the numbers came right again and the invitation was issued, Lady Infill surprised herself by saying, 'We missed you last year. You must tell us *all* you have been up to since.'

There was a little pause before the reply came, but it was an acceptance. Daisy Flagg said that she had missed them, too, and would be arriving as usual after attending the early celebration of Holy Communion. It was to be hoped, she added that, as usual, there would be no inclement weather for her hundred-mile drive.

And then, over the answerphone on Christmas morning bleary-eyed Gervais pressing the button as he stood, yawning, over the kettle for the early-morning tea – came Daisy's voice saying she hoped it would be all right but she was bringing someone with her.

'Of course it's not all right,' screamed Lady I. 'Call her back immediately.'

'She's at church. The Early Celebration.'

'I don't care what celebration. She can't just land here with someone. We'll be thirteen again.'

'Maybe we could get in the vicar.'

'We don't know a vicar.'

'Maybe,' said Auntie Pansy hopefully, 'I could go to my London club?'

They quarrelled their way through breakfast, through the stuffing of the turkey, through the creation of gravies and bacon rolls, through the endless trimming and cleansing of sprouts. They sulked and fumed and drank a lot of wine and began to say that Daisy Flagg was a pain, always had been a pain, always would be, and why had they got her? They'd had the chance to be shot of her. They'd let it go. Who was she anyway? Nobody had ever known. It was all their mother's fault. Playing the eccentric *grande dame*. Years out of date. Egalitarian rubbish.

'And we all know who your mother was,' said Sukey. 'Nobody.'

They sat at the table in disarray.

Turkey over, there was still no Daisy.

'Maybe she's had a crash on the motorway at last,' said someone.

But it was after half-past two by this time and nobody quite dared to say, 'Let's hope', for they were now disquieted.

'She'll swan in with the nuts,' said someone else. 'You'll see. She's probably bringing a man. She's probably married.'

But she wasn't married. Daisy Flagg the parasite never married.

Miss Mistletoe *married*? Ridiculous!

Towards the end of the orange and lemon sugar slices and the coffee, the limp wagging of the crackers, came the sound of the motor car upon the dying winter afternoon. It came into view, spluttering and clanking, between the stark branches of the avenue and jerked to a halt below the terrace.

And out of it sprang a shining-faced and stocky Daisy Flagg with a three-month-old baby in her arms, and she took her place at table and put this baby on her knee.

'So *terribly* late,' she said. 'Such *terrible* trouble with sparking plugs,' and she grinned. 'She's terribly hungry. D'you mind if I do this at table?'

And Miss Mistletoe upped with her smock and her T-shirt to reveal amazing bounty beneath.

Jane Gardam's collection of short stories, *Missing the Midnight*, is published by Sinclair-Stevenson.

Sara Wheeler

WHITE CHRISTMAS

IN THE EARLY DAYS of Antarctic exploration, when the great white south was still a featureless immensity languishing at the bottom of the map, the men who sailed off to give it a history recorded their lives on the ice in daily diary entries. As for everyone away from home, Christmas was an especially poignant time for the explorers, and as it falls in midsummer in the Antarctic, they were invariably out sledging. Summer notwithstanding, December was often a brutally cold month, and many Christmases were spent simply surviving. That the men kept up their spirits in intolerable conditions, often looking death in the eye, is a testament to what the human spirit can achieve.

Here are three of my favourite diary entries.

On Christmas Day 1902, during the *Discovery* expedition, Captain Scott, Bill Wilson and Ernest Shackleton were outward-bound from Hut Point on their first sledging journey south. Here is Scott, writing in his diary after the evening meal of hoosh (a one-pot hot meal, typically of pemmican with broken up biscuits, always served by a blind and therefore impartial distribution of portions called 'Shut-eye'):

> For a week we have looked forward to this day with childish delight, and long before that decided that it would be a crime to go to bed hungry on Christmas night, so the week went in planning a gorgeous feed. We laid ourselves out for supper reckless of consequences, having first had a Christmas wash and brush-up. Redolent of soap, we sat around the cooking pot, whilst into its boiling contents was poured a double

whack of everything. In the hoosh that followed, one could stand the spoon with ease, and still the primus hissed on. Meanwhile, I had observed Shackleton ferreting around in his bundle, out of which he presently produced a spare sock, and stowed away in the sock was a small round object about the size of a cricket ball which, when brought to light, proved to be a noble plum pudding. Another dive into his lucky bag and out came a crumpled piece of artificial holly. Heated in the cocoa, our plum pudding soon stood on the cooker lid with its decoration. For once we divided food without 'Shut-eye'.

I am writing over my second pipe. The sun is still circling our small tent in a cloudless sky. The air is warm and quiet and all is pleasant without, and within we have a sense of comfort we have not known for many a day. We shall sleep well tonight, no dreams, no tightening of the belt.

Exactly nine years later, five members of Roald Amundsen's Norwegian expedition had just become the first men ever to stand at the South Pole. On Christmas Day, ahead of schedule, the jolly team reach their first supply cache on the return journey to base camp. They have so much fuel that they are able to light the primus just for the luxury of warmth.

Oscar Wisting collected biscuit crumbs, added powdered milk and created a traditional Norwegian rice porridge. In his diary that night he wrote:

> Now they are lighting the candles at home. We are there also, though the distance is great. But wait a little – it won't be long before we are home, and then it will be with victory in our hands.

Wisting's team mate Olav Bjaaland was obviously more mindful that they still had 600 miles to go. His Christmas Day diary entry reads: 'My friends at home, you don't need to envy me yet.'

On the same day, only a few hours skiing away, five Britons from Scott's Terra Nova expedition were en route to the Pole, unaware that the Norwegians had beaten them to it. Already hopelessly behind schedule, they were malnourished and exhausted. Birdie Bowers' diary for 25 December reads:

> Scott got fairly wound up and went on and on. My breath kept fogging my glasses, and our windproofs grew increasingly warm. Altogether, things were pretty rotten. At last Captain Scott stopped, and we found we had done fourteen and three quarter miles. And he said 'What about fifteen miles for Christmas Day?' So we gladly went on: anything definite is better than indefinite trudging.

In the early days of the new year they did make it to the Pole. When they saw the Norwegian flag flapping in the polar breeze, Scott wrote in his diary, 'The worst has happened.' It was to be their last Christmas.

Sara Wheeler's *Terra Incognita: Travels in Antarctica* is published by Vintage.

Michael Holroyd

CHRISTMAS

MY FAMILY saw Christmas as an opportunity for disaster. We had the recipe for disaster as other families had it for brandy butter. From the mince pies irretrievably lost in the garage to the crashing problem of washing-up in the kitchen, disasters crowded our day. We simply did not have the trick of celebrating things. We did our best We lit a fire in the hall, stoked up the Aga cooker in the kitchen, and deposited various gas-fire contraptions erupting with dangerous blue flames in passages. and on landings. But the house remained freezing and we usually all had flu. This was treated by my grandfather who was 'better than any doctor'. We never bothered to call in a doctor unless one of the dogs was ill.

I was brought up by my grandparents and the problem of 'what to do with the boy' was most acute at Christmas. We never solved it. One Christmas my aunt took me to a pantomime and I waited angrily for the pandas to appear, having understood it to be a *panda-mime*. Another Christmas, late at night, I secretly hung up a stocking at the end of my bed, having heard at school that people did this. Nothing happened. From which I learnt that you could not really believe what you were told at school. It was one of the most valuable lessons Christmas taught me.

Michael Holroyd is the author of several acclaimed biographies. His most recent *Augustus John*, is published by Vintage.

John Burnside

CHILDREN SLEDDING IN THE DARK, MAGDALEN GREEN

We have studied the colours of night:
loan-path ambers, hedges dipped in
    bronze,
jade-tinted snow

and nothing is wholly true
till we believe:
the sky is glass, the distance is a train,

angels are sealed in the gaps
of walls, their fledged wings
spreading through mortar,

and under the lamps, possessed by the
    pull of the dark,
these children hold the glow
of the imagined,

perfect and hard, arriving at copper or
    gold
by guesswork; trusting what's
    contrived in flesh
to echo in the rooms of gravity.

John Burnside's latest collection of poetry, *A Normal Skin*,
and his first novel, *The Dumb House*, are both published by
Jonathan Cape.

Howard Marks

THOUGHTS ON CHRISTMAS

FINDING OUT the reality behind Christmas was the first proof I'd encountered of my parents' ability to tell fibs for the sake of something held by them to be more sacramental than mere truth: caring (giving presents and helping out) and faith (believing something despite vast evidence to the contrary). But what's the deal with a North Pole resident called Santa Claus upstaging infidel magic carpet rides and making witches broomstick flights look like wanking with a piece of wood? This guy delivers your annual dope supplies on a flying trolley operating on several reindeer power. There's no chance of being busted, even if the cops are watching: he delivers down the chimney. Then there's mince pies, holly, King Wenceslas, crackers, trees, and puddings, to say nothing of making love under mistletoe and virgins giving birth in stables under shiny stars guiding wise Eastern kings.

At the very least, Christmas is meant to be a celebration of the birth of someone called Jesus Christ. Some say he was both God and the Son of God, born through immaculate conception. Others say he was a deranged faggot. Many think he was just a cool travelling dude whose dad was a carpenter and whose mum was a sweet lady called Mary. But there wasn't much love around before Jesus Christ, not even in the Old Testament. He made us think about caring. A mild, peaceful, and pure guy, that's for sure. Gentle as a Lamb. While shepherds watched their flocks by night, Mary had a little lamb.

He turned water in wine, swallowed it, and asked to be remembered by others through their drinking it. He is the true vine. So let's have rivers of the Blood of Christ. Let it flow. Get off your face, and see God. That's what the early Christians must have done. The first Christian kingdom was ancient Britain under King Arthur before the English (Angles), French (Saxons) and Germans (Vikings, kind of) grabbed it. Those gallant knights of the round table got well stoned and tenaciously devoted themselves to the discovery of the Holy Grail, a goblet containing an inexhaustible supply of mind bending red wine. Why are we these days expected to drink at communion, very infrequently, a mere thimbleful of sickly liquid not as potent as the average shite lager? What kind of communication is that? It's a conspiracy between the Church and the breweries. Even when reindeers do their thing in the sky, Rudolf is allowed to get plastered and show off his red nose.

The Bible indicates Christ to be a water walking, non mistletoe eating, Pisces (fisher of men) with a guest pass to all the hip, exclusive, and high places. So why make out he was a non-floating, earthbound druid born as a Capricorn in December? The answer to this and most other Yuletide enigmas derives from our sincere concern to keep the heathens happy and on our side.

'Do what you want, guys. Get under the mistletoe, screw and sacrifice a virgin or two, drink your booze, let there be grass, smoke your Moses burning bush, eat your psilocybin mushrooms, get wasted, but remember, the whole affair is called Christmas, not winter solstice. Get spending. Give me a few quid, and I'll hook you up with Santa himself.'

Howard Marks' autobiography, *Mr Nice*, is published by Minerva.

John King

A Pint of Best

WHEN I WAS A boy I had two chances to see George Best play. The first was for Man United against Chelsea at Stamford Bridge and the second for Northern Ireland against England at Wembley, both in the early seventies. Sadly, George had more interesting things to do than kick a ball around in the mud, so I thought I'd missed out.

The girls used to link arms in the playground and march around singing 'Georgie Best, super star, wears frilly knickers and a Platex bra' (to the tune of *Jesus Christ Super Star*), but even so, he was someone we always hoped would move to Chelsea and link up with Peter Osgood, Alan Hudson and Charlie Cooke. There were rumours that Best fancied a move to the King's Road, but it never happened till his playing days were over.

Boxing Day 1976 saw Chelsea play Fulham at the Bridge, and with Best and Bobby Moore turning out for the Cottagers in the twilight of their careers it looked like it was going to be third time lucky, an extra Christmas present. Best really was as big a star as history paints him, and even though I supported Chelsea I still hoped he would play.

The crowd that Boxing Day was 55,003, the three being me, Steve Thorman and Steve Nickless – all of us school-kid boot boys with our silk scarves and DMs, and me with a Bowie cut. The Shed was packed with thousands of boot boys enjoying the Christmas spirit and Chelsea on a roll with Eddie McCreadie the manager of a young home-grown team that would be promoted at the end of the season. The club was struggling to stay in business and there was no money available for transfers.

There was a close bond between the fans and the team in those days, many of who were themselves Chelsea supporters. There were regular collections by the fans to help the club, with Save The Bridge buckets collecting coins before and after home games and on the away trains. I worked in Tesco two nights a week and put my coins in even though money was scarce – like thousands of others.

Looking back to those days and seeing how businessmen have been allowed to hijack football in the nineties shows there is no loyalty or respect on the part of football's administrators. Football's culture and history has been sold to the highest bidder, but in those days football really was special.

While modern middle-class pledges of loyalty don't stretch much further than the word processor and a freelance cheque, a lot of those Shed boys have grown up and will be there this Christmas, paying through the nose for a seat and charged £20 to have their picture taken with the FA Cup. Christmas Past doesn't get a second thought in the Premiership.

In 1976–77, Ray Wilkins was enjoying his second full season in the Chelsea side and everything he hit seemed to find the net. The Shed was very lively, and when Best trotted out and Steve Nickless was chucked out by the police I knew it was going to be a good day out. The game was nothing special, a 2–0 win for Chelsea, but gave us another couple of important points in the battle to regain our rightful place among the First Division elite.

Jingle Bells was a Christmas favourite in The Shed along with the more usual Hello Hello Chelsea Aggro. The Shed was a great place to watch a game from as a kid. It was noisy, crushed and there was a lot of humour. Those people who slag it off do so from a distance. The Shed was special and the thousands of Chelsea fans who grew up there will say the same thing.

The old home terraces have been knocked down now and replaced with state-of-the-art plastic seats. Instead of The Shed, The Stretford End, The Kop and The Loft, we get a succession of passionless corporate names.

After the game it was the usual walk to Fulham Broadway where you could take your feet off the ground and the pressure of the surrounding crowd meant you were carried to the station. Then it was the tube to Earls Court with the inevitable delay in the tunnel as the crowds were cleared up ahead, the painful Bank Holiday service to Rayners Lane, a long wait in the cold, then the Metropolitan Line back to Uxbridge. The world was deserted, but you'd done the Christmas pilgrimage.

Usually when we got back to Uxbridge after a home game we'd have some chips then, if we had the money, a couple of pints in one of the less-fussy local pubs not too bothered about age. But this was Boxing Day and there was no room at the Inn, let alone chips. We had a two-mile walk home because there weren't any buses.

It was freezing and we'd missed the Boxing Day food, but I knew Mum would have something left over and, anyway, we'd just seen Chelsea win 2–0. On top of that, I'd finally got to see George Best play. As we walked home shivering I expect George was sitting in the warm celebrating Christmas in style, but we didn't care, he was one of the great players and well worth the 50p admission.

John King's novel *Headhunters* is published by Jonathan Cape. His previous book, *The Football Factory*, is available in Vintage.

Irvine Welsh

DREAMING OF A WHITE CHRISTMAS

KEASBO IS SITTING in an armchair in his dingy flat. It's cold – very, very cold – but he's too skagged-up to notice. On the couch Jackie, his girlfriend of however many days it was since he came into a quality bit of gear, is starting to get strung out in front of the telly. The Pope is on the box with a Christmas message of peace.

– Hear that auld cunt: fuckin wanker. Aw they cunts, thir aw fuckin wankers, Keasbo sneers.

– Needin mair skag Keasbo, eh . . . Jackie says, breathlessly, shivering, realising that now the acknowledgement has been made, the suffering will remorselessly rev up until her needs will have to be met.

Keasbo can't hear her. He is still animated, as he tends to be when he comes into some China White instead of the more common brown. It's always his custom to mix it up with a bit of speed. For some reason he never does this with the broon stuff. That's Johnny Swan's way: he being the party whom Keasbo has scored the white from.

As Jackie pleads, Keasbo continues scrutinising the Pope. Fuckin cunt. A brief sectarian impulse flashes through his mind, an old tape being replayed. But it isn't the one Keasbo is looking for. He moves on and a vague recollection forms in his head and quickly crystallises and spouts into a fully-fledged tale that needs telling. – Did ah ever tell ye what happened when that auld fucker went tae one ay they South American countries? He gestures dismissively at the box, oblivious to Jackie's contorting face. – The daft cunt goes ower tae these Indian punters fae this tribe, and these boys gie um a bound copy ay the bible wi an inscription in thair lingo, oan the fron ay it likes. So the auld wanker's aw chuffed until one ay his aides tells urn what the inscription says: TAKE YOUR FUCKIN BOOK BACK. IT'S BROUGHT US NOTHING BUT POVERTY AND MISERY. Ha ha ha, Keasbo laughs coldly, the laughter of a guy with his mates rather than his bird, which he becomes aware of and which makes him feel a little uneasy, but he has started so he's finishing. – That's tellin they cunts. Ha ha ha.

Jackie is not impressed. She pulls some strands of long, greasy brown hair from her face and fastens them behind her ear where she hopes they will stay. The contact of her cold hand makes her ear throb and burn. She shudders again. – Skag Keasbo . . . ah'm sufferin here. Ah'm needin a fuckin fix, eh Keasbo . . .

Keasbo recognises that, although he isn't sick yet, Jackie's unremitting insistence on charting her own decline will inevitably precipitate his. He'd best get sorted soon, while he still can. It is Christmas Eve tomorrow. This means that everybody will be away. It always strikes him that the most unlikely people – dealers, junkies, wasters, whom he could never imagine sitting down to a turkey dinner with the family – did in fact, invariably vanish at this time of the year. He has a brief vision of Johnny Swan and Seeker topped by party hats pulling a cracker together, one all rotten teeth, the other a deadpan expression. The cracker splits apart like a flashbulb igniting and everyone is covered in white powder. – A white Christmas . . . he says softly to himself. Yes, everybody went to their families. Everybody except Keasbo. Not after the last time.

– Keith, c'moan! Jackie pleads.

– Aye, ah'm fucked n aw, he acknowledges. – Ye goat hirey's? He looks at her urgently, but more in hope than in expectation.

– Naw.

Keasbo feels a surge of anger. He is financing her habit as well as his own. What fuckin use was she? He hudnae even shagged her yet. The old holy papa's goat mair chance ay getting ehs hole than me, Keasbo thinks. Fuckin hell, a loat mair ay a chance given the shite ye read aboot Priest's cowpin everything in sight.

– Ah've burned every fucker doon. Swaney'll no let ays through the door n Seeker'll want cash up front. Huv tae hit ma sister, at that sheltered housing scheme, eh.

– Will she gie ye any money? Jackie asks, her face hard and eyes penetrating.

– Aye, course she will, Keasbo says emphatically, before realising that it's been a long time since he's seen Susan. Oh God, it was last Christmas and that had been the first time in three years, although he'd been inside before that. A prison sentence did that: stopped you getting out and about. Susan though, she'd never come and visit him back then. Just acted normal when he got out, like he had never been inside. Then last Christmas, at the auld man and auld lady's he'd fucked it up there alright. Fucked it in the service of junk. Here he was though, he was doing it again, resurrecting the ghosts of Christmas past. – Ah mean surely tae fuck aye, eh. Ah mean Christmas; time fir faimlay n aw that shite, he considers, trying to force resolve into his tone.

– Hurry then Keith, Jackie urges. She wants him right on the case and back with a result before all this gets too much. She bunches up in her chair, drawing her knees to her chest and crushing a threadbare cushion under her chin. The wait was ahead. Always the wait.

– Too right doll. Be a white Christmas eftir aw eh? Or a broon yin anywey. Keasbo looks searchingly at her again. Junk has blunted her looks and sexuality but sometimes a certain gesture or expression showed him where they had been. Aye, there's quality fanny lurking under the surface of this grey, sweating, bent figure and no mistake, he calculates. – Tell ye what . . . see whin ah git back . . . mibee a wee ride, eh Jackie? Keasbo ventures, experimenting more with his own reactions than hers. It's been a while since he's had sex. He'd gone in for it in a big way when he came back out the nick, but then he'd got back on the junk and it just faded into the background. He tried to attach some kind of value to it, first through the recall of sexual experiences, then via their absence, but it was like it had never happened for him. Never had it, never missed it, he thinks with a faint smile. Finding his libido was like trying to tune into a radio station with a poor signal and a terrible reception. If you concentrated hard enough and were deft enough you could occasionally pick it up, but it never lasted and was invariably drowned out by the other stations which surrounded it with their twenty-four hour blaring SKAG.

– Aye . . . right. Jist git the gear, Jackie says. The thought of Keasbo's cock inside her fills her with something staggering slowly towards the state of apathy.

Keasbo gets the message, not from her but from his pain centres which tingle in preparation for a more sustained onslaught. He hauls himself out of the armchair and leaves the room. In the lobby he puts on his old overcoat and takes a deep breath before heading out the door and down the stairs. Keasbo wants to build up a head of steam which will take him from the top of Leith Walk to Gorgie and back but as he emerges from the stair door into the street a group of young kids start pelting him with snowballs, shouting at him:
– Junkie! Fuckin junkie!

– Fuckin wide wee cunts! Keasbo snaps, but without breaking his stride, still hurrying down the snowy pavement.

— Junkie, junkie, his baws urnae spunky . . . the kids sing in a malevolent rhyme.

Keasbo looks back at this. The kids had dug in closer to the bone that time. – Fuck off ya wee cunts! Ah'd fuckin shag everyone ay youse wee bastards tae death!

One snowball hits his shoulder and the cold water trickles down the inside of his collar. Keasbo shudders but he doesn't even attempt to give chase, he just carries on around the corner to the main road where he waits at the bus stop. Fortunately for him, he doesn't have to wait too long. The bus is trundling through the snow up the Walk. He gets on and sits in the disabled seat without even bothering to show the disinterested driver his out-of-date pass. The withdrawal is kicking in and he is shaking and feverish as the bus ambles towards the city centre.

The city goes past him and Keasbo is a bit disconcerted to note that he can't make out anything through the dirty windows of the bus and the white glare of snow, only the odd, darkened, smudge of a passer-by. It could be the fuckin North Pole ootside, he thinks. The bus turns sharply and he is pushed forward in his seat. Now though, he can recognise Haymarket and the narrow, main thoroughfare of Dalry Road. Once again Keasbo starts to think about shagging. Keasbo considers the city and thinks of all the places he like to put his cock: if Leith Walk is Edinburgh's giving, generous fanny, then Gorgie Road and Dalry Road are its arsehole, a long, tight-as-fuck shit-tube. He thinks this is a bit indulgent but he knows that he loves the city so much that one day he'd just like to take it to bed with him and fuck it every way.

Keasbo gets off the bus in Gorgie Road. He walks a little, slipping and almost falling over in the snow, but managing to correct himself. The cold is now biting, but he is more aware of his pulse playing strange rhythms in different parts of his body. His organic tissue feels saturated with toxins.

He comes upon a gleaming, granite new-build structure which is the sheltered housing complex, and he enters it through double doors. The rush of warm air from the central heating system and the sharp and stale smell of old bodies it carries blasts him. Striding down a long corridor Keasbo notes a dining room which is full of elderly people, seated around a set table.

Going next door to a substantial kitchen, he sees his sister Susan, red and sweaty as she lifts a tray of food out of a big oven on to a worktop. She is looking harassed, wearing oven gloves and an apron, and has still not noticed Keasbo.

– Eh Sooz, he says, slightly timidly. He has always been in some awe of his sister. She is five years older than him and has always epitomised straightness and organisation. He thinks of them as kids. She wasn't cruel, but she knew how to set him up for some hidings. Then again, he must have been a pain in the arse at times. And now here he was again. It was good not to grow up, but maybe sometimes you could not grow up in the wrong way. Life, he reflects, quickly smothering that maverick thought with a psychic blanket before it burned too deeply.

– Keith! Long time no see, Susan says, turning and seeming genuinely pleased to see him. Keasbo's anticipation level rises.

– Thank god n aw, she continues. His smile broadens. It's been a long time since the word 'Keith' preceeded the term 'Thank God', at least in his presence. – Look, ah'm up tae ma eyes in it here. Everybody else is oaf sick and ah'm huvin tae gie the auld folks their Christmas lunch. You can make yirself useful and serve the sherry.

She points to glasses of sherry stacked on a huge, oval-shaped silver tray before going back to the oven and producing a large turkey which she dumps on a table.

Keasbo's spirits have fallen. He looks at the silver tray, the glasses of sherry and then back at his sister. This won't do. Keasbo's here on urgent business, not to fanny about with auld cunts and their sherry. The concept strikes him as not so much alien as inappropriate. – Eh Sooz, um a bit short likesay . . .

Susan's not hearing him though. She picks up the sherry tray and moves towards him. – Christ ye look terrible. Huv you goat that flu virus n aw? she asks, trying to scrutinise beyond the wasted image that confronts her.

Keasbo shifts under that gaze of old. – Aye, it's a killer, he agrees, – Eh, ah forgoat tae go tae the bank . . . kin ye lend ays some dosh? Jist fir the morn.

– We'll see, she says, thrusting the tray at him, forcing him to take it, – but you've goat tae gie the auld yins their sherry! Ah'm up tae ma eyes in it! Aw hands tae the pump, she urges.

– Aye but . . . Keasbo protests in a biscuit-ersed manner. He feels himself eight years old again, trailing in her gum-chewing adolescent slipstream. She'd assumed a mantle of certainty in his eyes at that time, and had never let it slip since then.

– Take the tray through! Susan commands. – And some ay

they auld yins kin be funny, so mind and serve it right!

Keasbo obeys without further questioning, though he's shaking as he finds himself going through the connecting doors into the dining room. The glasses seem to slide with each step he takes. The old folks stop their chatter and survey him in a disapproving silence. One woman with a twisted lower lip positively glowers.

Through his wretchedness and the hostile reception he receives, Keasbo struggles to affect a saccharine cheerfulness. – The sherry is served . . . he announces with as much of a grandiose flourish as he can manage.

The woman with the twisted lip turns to her neighbour and hisses, – Look at um Jessie, ehs shakin . . . ehs spillin aw the sherry . . .

Jessie, looking cold in spite of the thick woollen cardigan she is wearing, nods fervently and announces to the table in a high, shrill, indignant voice, – Eh cannae stoap bloody well shakin! The sherry's spillin! She points accusingly at Keasbo. Then she herself visibly shivers, as if the presence of this evil spirit is frosting over her bones.

But the sherry *is* spilling. Keasbo is oscillating on the spot. He just wants to dump the tray on the table so they can help themselves and he can fuck off, but not one of the old cunts is clearing a space for him, some of them have their fuckin handbags on it for fuck's sakes. But now he's more aware of it than ever before, the fact that he's sick, just so fuckin sick, he's trembling miserably and he sees the looks of hatred boring into him from the occupants of the table . . .

An old guy in a suit, one of only two men at the table, looks disgustedly at Keasbo, unshaven as he is and wrapped in his scabby old overcoat. – That bloody mess servin us oor Christmas din . . . he stutters as Keasbo tries to lower the tray to the table but loses control and the glasses slide off and topple like British soldiers at the Somme, spilling their blood-red contents all over Jessie and her neighbour.

– Oh my god! One woman shrieks, then bursts into tears.

– Look at um! Jessie's dress! He's bloody well ruined it! The woman with the lip shouts as Jessie hyperventilates.

Keasbo looks at the carnage on the table and then at the sea of lynch-mob faces. The cursing and moaning of the old folks becomes a background cacophony as he raises his gaze above their heads, focusing on a picture on the wall. It's Greyfriars Bobby, that wee dug, he thinks. Then he can sense his sister Susan running in and gasping and getting a cloth and ineffectively dabbing at sherry-soaked laps. He lowers his gaze. From the depths of his tormented soul he lets rip with an almighty roar, digging his elbows into his side to force out the angst as well as to stabilise himself – SHUT THE FUCK UP YA STUPID AULD CUNTS! YIS IR AW FUCKIN WELL GAUNNY BE DEID SOON SO WHIT UR YIS FUCKIN WELL WORRYIN ABOOT YA MINGIN AULD BASTARDS! AH HOPE IT'S YIR LAST FUCKIN CHRISTMAS YA FUCKIN SMELLY AULD CUNTS! NAE WONDER YIR FUCKIN FAIMLAYS DIDNAE WANT YIS THIS CHRISTMAS! FUCK YIS! GIT A FUCKIN WASH! A'HM OOT AY HERE. AH CANNAE STAND THE SMELL AY PISH COMIN FAE YIS!

There is a brief silence. Keasbo suffused with a new energy, turns on his heels and runs out of the complex down the road, scarcely aware of the cold air.

Keith! What's wrong! What happened? What have ye done! Susan has followed him and is shouting after him.

– You kin fuck off n aw! Jist fuck off! he turns and snaps at her, flailing the air with the back of his hand. A startled man and woman passing by quickly cross over to the other side of the road. Susan stands rooted to the spot, bristling with indignation. She then turns and runs back into the complex, holding her jacket together with one hand, her free arm swinging stiffly, as if operating like a rudder as she heads to her destination.

Keasbo's spirits dip. He realises that he has come away empty-handed. As soon as this thought sinks home, he is moving with the same purpose, but back in the direction he just came from. – Sooz! Ah'm sorry Sooz! he pleads, running after her. He bangs on the glass doors of the complex which Susan has locked behind her. She is facing him sternly through the glass. – Ah sais ah wis sorry . . . he implores.

– You git away fae here Keith Halcrow or ah'll phone the polis masel! See if a willnae!

– Jist gies a score Sooz! Fir Christmas n that! Goan! Keasbo begs,

– GO-OH-OHNN! he beseeches her, but Susan is unyielding. She then moves out of his vision and she is replaced by a pack of scornful malevolent old faces.

– CUNTS! Keasbo shouts. – FUCKIN CUNTS!

Then it hits him that Susan may very well be going to phone the police, so he legs it back down the road.

Keasbo rushes down the street for a few yards, his mind buzzing and his body feeling sick and twisted. Sitting down and trembling on a cold park bench, he wraps his arms around himself and tries to gather his thoughts. Then in a surge of inspiration he realises that his brother Gary lives within walking distance at Harrison Gardens.

Gary, though, represents an even worse bet than Susan, he thinks to himself. We dinnae get oan. The cunt willnae even let ays in the fuckin hoose. He's probably no even in anyway. Keasbo's considering all this while at the same time heading as fast as his legs can take him in the direction of Harrison Gardens. No, they didn't get on, but it was Christmas. Gary would surely be good for a double score.

Gary is in. His face falls with the same level of elasticity that serves to snap Keasbo's into a crinkle of a smile when the siblings confront each other on the doorstep. – Keith . . . eh, come in . . .

– Gaz, Keasbo nods, walking past him into the flat and heading for the front room.

– How ye daein? Gary says, trying to battle against the resignation in his voice.

– No bad . . . eh, jist daein a wee bit ay Christmas visitin . . . been doon the road tae see Sooz n that, ken it the sheltered housin?

Gary looks at him for a second, then shakes his head miserably. – Yir no back oan that shite again, are ye?

– Naw, ah jist thought wi it bein Christmas . . .

– Aye right, Gary snaps. – Dinnae you be gaun roond tae ma Ma's. Right? Ah'm fuckin well warning ye. She disnae need that shite oafay you again!

Keasbo looks at his brother. It irritates him how he appropriates their parents in that way, excluding him. But he couldn't bullshit Gary. While Susan ignores his condition, Gary was invariably straight to the point. Too fuckin straight to the point, Keasbo thinks, too fuckin eager to emphasise the difference between them. – Look, ah need some dough for Christmas. Ah'm skint . . . ah jist thought . . .

Gary considers breaking into a lecture, one he prepares in his head about once a week, but as he has delivered it so many times before, he knows that it will do no good. Yvonne would be back from work soon and she would flip if she found this fucker here. The priority therefore was to get him out of the house, but keep him away from Ma's. There was only one way to do it and that way involved no gain to him. – Much dae ye need? he asks wearily.

– A ton, Keasbo ventures assertively, his junkie's mercenary understanding of the power dynamics between them honed to perfection. Gary had blown it when he'd mentioned their Ma.

– Eh! It's fuckin Christmas Keith!

– Ah widnae ask but . . .

– Aw right! But ah'm gaunny have tae go tae the cashpoint, Gary says sulkily.

Keasbo feels a massive surge of elation. – Ah'll chum ye! he volunteers with enthusiasm.

– Naw, you'll have tae stey here wi the bairn, Gary warily states, gesturing him to come into the kitchen. A toddler in a high chair was pushing a spoon around a bowl of food. It's Keasbo's niece, and he's only seen her once before.

– Hiya doll, mind ay me? Uncle Keith? he asks in a cold and brisk manner. Keasbo thinks about this for a split second, and is almost embarrassed at the difference between what he said and how it came out. The child just looks at him quizzically.

– You mind ay yir Uncle Keith! Course ye do.

Gary smiles coffin-plate style and then steals a doubtful

look at his brother before ruffling his daughter's fine hair. He feels an internal twinge of fear then hate at the recognition that they are both his flesh. Shuddering inside he feels the possibility of all his unspoken ambitions for his child crash against the wasted rock that is his brother. Yet it is his brother. That has to count for something, though at this stage Gary can't think what.

– Ah want ma puddin. The little girl says.

– Gie her her sweet, Gary instructs Keasbo. – It's in the fridge. He shakes his head again, and kisses the little girl. – Back in a minute Princess, he says, pulling on a quilted jacket and heading out. – See she eats it, he adds as he departs.

More fuckin servitude, Keasbo thinks anxiously, but he can't really complain. – Now whaire's that sweet, Keasbo wonders out loud, looking at the fridge. There are magnets stuck on the front of it. They're offensively tacky and bright and this is a different world. He's feeling ugly and ill. He opens up, and inside the fridge there's a chocolate dessert in a bowl. It's sprinkled with hundreds and thousands.

His hands still trembling, Keasbo brings it over to his niece and sits down beside her. He takes a spoonful of dessert and holds it up to the child. It quivers. – Gaunny eat this? he almost pleads.

The child shakes her head slowly, emphatically and negatively. – Dinnae like they bits, she says, pointing at the yellow hundred and thousands with distaste.

– Fuck, Keasbo curses softly.

– Take them away! The little girl commands.

Keasbo starts to use the edge of the spoon to extract the yellow hundreds and thousands from the dessert, but his hand is shaky and some of the red and pink and blue ones come off as well. The child watches every move intently.

– Keep them! Keep the red! she screeches in horror.

– Fuckin wee bastard . . . ah'll fuckin . . . Keasbo tightens his grip on the spoon, twisting it into the dessert and wilfully stirring it into a pulp. – THERE'S YIR DESSERT YA FUCKIN SPOILT WEE BASTARD!

He springs from the table as the child's lungs explode into

98

a long, ragged scream. Keasbo can't handle this. He storms out of the flat and into the stairwell. As he is heading down the stair, his brother is on his way back and they meet face on.

– Keith, Gary says in shock, – what's the fuckin score! Ye left the bairn oan her ain! Ye left the fuckin bairn!

– Naw Gaz, naw, the bairn's sound. A jist felt a wee bit dizzy needed some air . . . ye goat the hirey's?

Gary shakes his head in slow disgust. Keasbo says nothing, as his brother looks at him in a hurt, bewildered way. – Ye wir gaunny leave the bairn! he whimpers.

Keasbo stays silent, letting Gary maintain his look of loathing and betrayal as he pulls out the wad. Keasbo attempts to look suitably ashamed as his brother hands the money over. Gary would expect it. Later, the shame would be real, but right now junk need has expunged it from his emotional vocabulary. All he can think about is the journey back to Leith and Seeker's China White. – Cheers Gaz, he says, and is already bouncing down the steps before his brother can respond. – Merry Christmas, Keasbo shouts into the stairwell without looking back or breaking his stride.

Getting out into the street he crosses over the footbridge at Slateford Road and runs down the steps and along Stewart Terrace. He sees the gleaming new stands of Tynecastle Park poking up beyond the sandblasted tenements.

Keasbo is now feeling as rough as fuck, but he is euphoric at having scored the dough. He's waiting as patiently as his throbbing cells will allow for the bus, right outside the Hearts football ground. One end is open and you can see right across the park into the new stands.

An old guy at the bus stop looks at him. – Thir supposed tae be buildin another yin at this side ay the groond. Ah've pit in ma complaint tae the council, cause ah stey in that tenement up thair, he says, pointing at the flats above them. Thirty-two years. The best view ay the game. Baith goals n four corners ay the pitch. Now they want tae obstruct ma view by buildin a bloody stand right ootside ma kitchen!

– Fuckin nerve, eh?

– Aye, too right, the old guy nods.

Keasbo has had enough of old cunts for one day. He can see the bus coming up ahead. This auld fucker was getting it tight. – Ah dinnae ken what the world's comin tae, he says, malevolence rising inside him, – a fitba club wantin tae provide decent facilities tae paying customers, selfishly disregardin the rights ay a moochin auld jakey cunt who's hud thousands ay quid worth ay free fitba fir thirty-five years. It's sad eh? He says, striding from the curb to meet the advancing bus.

– Fuck off ya cheeky wee bastard! Ah'm entitled tae ma rights! The old guy barks. – Ah ken the score!

Keasbo laughs and puts his money in the box on the bus. He turns back and gives the old guy the V-sign. – Merry Christmas ya fuckin auld tube n ah hope yir next shite's a hedgehog!

As Keasbo takes his seat at the back of the bus, he notes that the snow is falling heavily – Leith driver, he says softly to himself, in an arrogant public-school accent, then smirks.

– It's gaunny be a white Christmas right enough, he nods to a woman with a formidable pile of shopping who is sitting across from him.

– Looks like it, she smiles cheerfully.

– Surein it is, Keasbo laughs, giving the wad in his jeans pocket a reassuring tap.

Irvine Welsh's latest book, *Ecstasy*, is published by Vintage.

Acknowledgements

THE PUBLISHERS gratefully acknowledge permission from the following to reprint stories, poems or extracts from work in copyright and to print previously unpublished material:

Louis de Bernières for 'Mrs Griffiths and the Carol Singers' © Louis de Bernières 1996, first published in *Country Life*, 5 December 1996. John Burnside for 'Children Sledding in the Dark, Magdalen Green' from *A Normal Skin* © John Burnside 1997, published by Jonathan Cape. John Farman for 'Bah – Humbug! – or the Story of Christmas Past' © John Farman 1997. Stephen Fry for 'The Adventure of the Laughing Jarvey' from *Paperweight* © Stephen Fry 1992, published by Mandarin. Jane Gardam for 'Miss Mistletoe' from *Missing the Midnight: Hauntings and Grotesques* © Jane Gardam 1997, published by Sinclair-Stevenson. Jane Green for 'A Christmas Story' © Jane Green 1997. Rolf Harris for the extract from *Beastly Behaviour* © Rolf Harris 1997, published by Century. John Hegley for 'These Were Your Father's', 'Christmas' and 'Christmas with the Brother-in-law (Oh What Fun)' from *Family Pack* © John Hegley 1996, published by Methuen; and for 'Christmas Poetry' from *Two Sugars Please* © John Hegley 1993, published by Methuen. Michael Holroyd for 'Christmas' © Michael Holroyd 1997. John King for 'A Pint of Best' © John King 1997. Howard Marks for 'Thoughts on Christmas' © Howard Marks 1997. Victoria Mather and Sue Macarthy-Snape for 'Social Stereotype 164: The Last Minute Christmas Shopper; text © Victoria Mather 1997, illustration copyright

ACKNOWLEDGEMENTS

© Sue Macartney-Snape 1997. Jennifer Paterson for 'Christmas Pudding' from *Feast Days: Recipes from The Spectator* © Jennifer Paterson 1990, published by Ebury. Python (Monty) Pictures Ltd for the extract from *The Life of Brian* © Python (Monty) Pictures Ltd 1979, published by Mandarin. Sue Townsend for the extract from *The Secret Diary of Adrian Mole Aged 13¾* © Sue Townsend 1982, published by Methuen; and for the extract from *The Growing Pains of Adrian Mole* © Sue Townsend 1984, published by Methuen. Irvine Welsh for 'Dreaming of a White Christmas' from *Ahead of Its Time: A Clocktower Press Anthology*, edited by Duncan McLean © Irvine Welsh 1997, published by Jonathan Cape. Sara Wheeler for 'White Christmas' © Sara Wheeler 1997.